CONVERSATIONS IN STONE

A Celebration of Hugh Miller's Legacy

CONVERSATIONS IN STONE

A Celebration of Hugh Miller's Legacy

Edited by Larissa Reid and Elsa Panciroli

Foreword by James Robertson

THE
HUGH MILLER
WRITING
COMPETITION

The editors would like to thank our generous partners who have sponsored this publication - The Scottish Geodiversity Forum, The Friends of Hugh Miller, Edinburgh Geological Society and Scottish Natural Heritage - without whom this book would not have been possible.

We would like to acknowledge the support of the Andrew Tannahill Fund for the Furtherance of Scottish Literature at the University of Glasgow.

Further gratitude goes to the partners who have supported the Hugh Miller Writing Competition for the past four years.

CONTENTS

Editor's Note

This book is the result of years' worth of determination, creativity and perseverance. I'm not talking of myself, but rather of the work begun by Hugh Miller, that has been continued by many others to this day, to bring Scotland's world-class geoheritage to the forefront of the public's imagination. This book, and the two highly successful writing competitions that it celebrates, I hope will go some small way towards contributing to this wide-reaching goal.

I would like to thank a number of people personally for their contributions to this work and its surrounding projects. To Martin and Frieda Gostwick of The Friends of Hugh Miller for their warm friendship and unwavering support. To Angus Miller, Chair of the Scottish Geodiversity Forum, whose enthusiasm for highlighting the importance of Scotland's geological heritage to all has been a continuous source of inspiration to me in recent years. To the Forum Executive, the management committee of the Friends of Hugh Miller, and to their respective memberships, who believed in my ability to make a success of the Hugh Miller Writing Competition right from the start. To Norman Bissell, Simon Cuthbert, Elsa Panciroli, Ruth Robinson, Kenny Taylor, and Janie Verburg, the judges for the writing competition, who have given up hours of their time to throw enthusiasm and fun into the proceedings. To all the competition partner organisations, for their generosity in donating prizes and for their help with publicity.

My co-editor for this book, Elsa Panciroli, deserves a medal for her patience, focus, and level-headed approach to finalising the project. Not to mention her glowing company over coffee and slices of cake! Also, my warm thanks to Matt Humpage, designer, for his beautiful cover art and his expertise in helping to collate the book. Thank you also to our illustrator and painter, Elizabeth Pickett, for her evocative watercolour illustrations.

My heartfelt thanks to all the contributors who have written stunning prose and poetry for this humble publication, and to all the friends I have made as a direct result of the Hugh Miller Writing Competition.

And finally, thank you to Hugh Miller, for blazing the trail we are all now following.

Larissa Reid, Autumn 2018

A Note of Thanks

Hugh Miller is one of these great figures of Scottish history who excites the imagination. When we walk in places such as the Isle of Eigg, the beaches of the Black Isle or indeed the streets of Edinburgh, we walk in his footsteps and can see the landscape through his eyes. He was not only a geologist; his ability to see the wider picture and recount it in a vivid and humorous way echoes through time. The Scottish Geodiversity Forum seeks to demonstrate the importance of Scotland's geology, not only what the rocks tell us about Scotland's past, but also geology's contribution to today's society, and the ongoing processes including climate change that will shape Scotland's future. Therefore, I am delighted that the Hugh Miller Writing Competition has been so successful in giving voice and direction to a host of talented writers who, by looking through the eyes of Hugh Miller, have created stories and poems based on Scotland's geology with resonance and relevance to today.

The success of projects like this rely on many things: the contributors, the inspirers, the judges. But most of all, at its heart are the small band of people who have made it work, whose vision and enthusiasm and voluntary effort have driven this endeavour. Especially that magical combination of the young Larissa Reid and the slightly less young Martin Gostwick, a combination for whom the word 'irrepressible' should have been invented. We look forward to more - much more - of this!

Angus Miller, Chair of the Scottish Geodiversity Forum

Foreword

By James Robertson

I was ten when I first visited Cromarty. My family was on holiday at Nigg on the northern shore of the Cromarty Firth (not long before that ancient settlement was changed almost beyond recognition by the oil industry) and one day we made the short ferry trip to visit Hugh Miller's cottage. As I leaned over the boat's side I spotted an enormous jellyfish, at least the size of a dustbin lid, going in the opposite direction. The next day, I found it on the beach at Nigg. I probably poked at it with a stick, but any further exploration was curtailed by childish squeamishness.

How different would have been the ten-year-old Hugh Miller's reaction? Even as a boy he was fascinated rather than repulsed by what he found in nature. As an adult he needed not just to marvel but to understand. In his *Sketch-Book of Popular Geology* he describes coming upon a stranded cuttlefish:

> The day was extremely calm; I heard a peculiar sound, - a *squelch*, if I may employ such a word; and there, a few yards away, was a loligo nearly two feet in length, high and

dry upon the pebbles. I laid hold of it by the sheath or sack; and the loligo, in turn, laid hold of the pebbles, just as I have seen a boy, when borne off against his will by a stronger than himself, grasping fast to projecting door-posts and furniture.

Immediately, Miller has our attention: the *Loligo* or cuttlefish is like us, although - as he has already said in the preceding paragraph - also *not* like us:

A man buried to the neck in a sack, and prepared for such a race as Tennant describes in his *Anster Fair*, is an exceedingly strange-looking animal, but not half so strange-looking as a strollach.

Miller was a knowledge geek. Everything he wrote is packed with information. In the few lines I have quoted he gives us both the scientific name (*Loligo vulgaris*) and a Gaelic name for squid (a cephalopodic relative of the cuttlefish), makes a literary reference and draws a memorable analogy to the animal's defensive instincts. And this is even before he takes out his penknife and performs a vivisection:

What follows the reader may deem barbarous; but the men who gulp down at a sitting half a hundred live oysters to gratify their taste, will surely forgive me the destruction of a single mollusc to gratify my curiosity.

It is impossible to stop reading at this point: Miller knew how to keep his readers' attention. Dipping in and out of his voluminous output is like wandering in a vast museum of everything. Natural history, literature, geology, folklore, social history, theology, politics, geography, travel, inventions, law, injustice - he covers it all, and makes connections everywhere: 'Life itself is a school, and Nature always a fresh study.' There is no separation in Miller's world view between science and the arts, or for that matter between science and faith. I think this is why, even though our knowledge today far outstrips what a self-taught working-man in early nineteenth century Scotland knew or could have known, he is still so readable. He constantly challenges the idea that life is made up of compartments that can be entered only with somebody else's permission. He is interested, so he enters.

This book contains poetry and prose inspired and illuminated by Hugh Miller's example. I am greatly impressed by the range and quality of the writing presented here and have little doubt, on the evidence of these pieces of work (Miller was keen on evidence!), that he will continue to work his magic on the curiosity and imagination of others for many years to come.

James Robertson, Spring 2019

'Our' Hugh Miller

BY MARTIN GOSTWICK

SECRETARY, THE FRIENDS OF HUGH MILLER

You know from the road signs as soon as you reach the outskirts that you have arrived at the 'Birthplace of Hugh Miller, geologist and writer'. And coming off the main road, you see at once the statue towering over the place, and realise that the figure atop must be the same man, Hugh Miller. Yet thousands upon thousands of first-time visitors to Cromarty down the decades have asked, 'Who was he, then?'

At the bicentenary of his birth in 2002, every child in the local primary school posed that question in their opera, purposely entitled 'Hugh Who?'. And they answered it - a man who heroically gave his life to hammer, chisel and pen, toiling until the torture in his lungs and his brain-diseased nightmares brought him down.

It was greatly moving, some ninety of these youngsters, finely trained by a professional theatre company, showing in song and dance with hammers on stone, chisels opening fossils, pen in hand, the story so well known to the entire community.

Visitors from afar soon receive enlightenment about 'who he was,' at the National Trust for Scotland's Museum in Miller House, and the Birthplace Cottage next door in Church Street, Cromarty. The two vividly contrasting buildings sit amidst the handsome merchants' villas which have led the neighbourhood to be described as an 18th Century time warp.

In Miller House they find the man who described himself as a 'sort of Robinson Crusoe' of geology, the first to discover utterly strange fossil fishes right on the shore not half a mile from his home, immediately to be acclaimed by his peers as a pioneer of natural science. From this beginning he amassed many thousands of specimens which after his death would contribute to the core of the country's national fossil collection, now held in the National Museum of Scotland, and still used by palaeontologists for research today.

They find a 'people's champion' who, as editor of his national newspaper, *The Witness*, helped to break the vice-like grip which landowners held, through patronage of ministers, over their tenants' spiritual life as well as temporal.

A champion also who, in his searing editorials, denounced the infamous Highland Clearances, and spoke up against the degrading living conditions of the rural poor and the newly industrialised working classes.

A voice for world peace, who condemned Britain's conduct of imperial conquest and wars as 'evil in all circumstances.' A voice for freedom and civil rights, demanding the 'right to roam,' and the release of sites for new churches. He held to principles honourable in any age. While a terrible foe in print, he behaved always, as far as the evidence tells us, as a tender and loving husband and father.

His thatched Birthplace Cottage in Cromarty bears witness to a life of childhood poverty following his sea-captain father's death in a shipwreck. It also holds the hearth around which he heard the stories of the past from his family and neighbours, which he would write down in his bedroom upstairs. Many years later these tales would result in his folkloric masterwork, *Scenes and Legends of the North of Scotland*. Walter Scott and Robert 'Rabbie' Burns were among his literary heroes, and the great English essayists served as his writing models. Reading and hearing tales of William Wallace confirmed his fervent patriotism.

From behind the cottage, it is a short climb up the raised beach to the great monument which captures the man's essence in stone. From below, you could mistake him for a Roman senator in a toga, but those at all familiar with his appearance recognise straightaway the plain shepherd's plaid he wore throughout his life. In his left hand he is examining a fossil, perhaps *Pterichthyodes milleri*, the Devonian era armour-plated fish which bears his name, and which is shown in sculpted form beneath his feet.

His right hand rests on a pile of books, which he either read or wrote himself. These must surely include *The Old Red Sandstone*, his most recognised geological work - soon to be republished after decades out of print. Then he will be revealed again as one of our most eloquent nature-writers, a visionary of deep time.

This is the very spot where he lay, a boy just five years old, waiting day after day for the sight of his father's ship coming home, in vain. It commands a view of the Cromarty and Moray Firths, and the two headlands, the North and South Sutors, which remain almost exactly as they were in his day. That view is a large part of what gives Cromarty its enchantment.

You have only to read Hugh Miller's autobiography, *My Schools and Schoolmasters*, to become immersed, as I did, in Cromarty's yesterdays as if they were still with us, thrilling - just like the rebel boy - in discovering the flora and fauna of the sands, rocks, caves and woods, en-visaging his adventures, or in re-imagining his legend-ary tales, or fossil-hunting in the deposits he opened to the world.

Cromarty is an amiable, neighbourly sort of place, as embodied in its motto, 'Mean weil, speak weil, do weil,' and exemplified, for instance, by Hugh's mother Harriet, who would always give a hungry neighbour a bite to eat, even when almost destitute herself. The town and its environs defined what Hugh Miller was about in all their aspects.

The question, 'Hugh Who?' still needs answering for far too many people today. Such a fascinating character, of significance not just as a prominent social historian and commentator in Scotland, but also for his incredible contribution to palaeontology, Hugh Miller should once again be a household name. Perhaps his untimely death by his own hand at the age of fifty-four should provide us with an opportunity to discuss mental health and su-icide in constructive ways? Perhaps a film of his extraor-dinary life would also help him achieve the wider rec-ognition he deserves? We hope that the republishing of some of his best work, the production of this book, and the new writing he inspires, will go some way towards bringing more people to appreciate this giant of Scottish science and literature. Our group seeks to do just this, and you would be most welcome to join us. You can find us at:

www.thefriendsofhughmiller.org.uk*

---

* The Hugh Miller Museum and Birthplace Cottage was saved from clo-sure in 2011 through a generous endowment made by Miller's great, great grand-daughter, the late Mrs Marian McKenzie Johnston.

Archipelagos of Thought

By Larissa Reid with Robert Macfarlane

In my hand, I'm holding a piece of bloodstone. Formed on what is now the Isle of Rùm in Scotland, this hazy green-blue, beautifully smooth rock was created in a basaltic lava flow stemming from the Skye volcanoes, which were active around fifty-eight million years ago. Bloodstone is a type of micro-grained mineral called chalcedony, and it forms when silica-rich water begins to crystalize, coating the solidified rims of gas bubbles within the lava. The fluid crystallises on the outer walls and forms a gel comprising twisted long fibres of two types of silica - moganite and quartz. It's a bit like the calcification of pipes*. Interestingly, chalcedony - rather beautifully pronounced 'chahl-SAID-oh-knee' - can show concentric banding like agates. Some pieces look like they have miniature landscapes held within them.

The name, bloodstone, comes from the flecks of red iron present as inclusions in the rock. Stories abound regarding this mineral – it was said to have been laid

---

* My thanks to Rachel Walcott, head of Earth Systems at the National Museum, Scotland for her input regarding bloodstone's formation.

at the feet of Christ on the cross, and that the flecks are blood from the crucifixion, hence another name, 'martyr's stone'. The Romans called it heliotrope, perhaps a nod to the fact that some pieces resemble a landscape infused with the colours of the setting sun. The piece I'm holding has no red flecks. It's sea-polished and completely smooth on one face. It's permanently cold to the touch and it's utterly compelling. It's the perfect size to fit snugly into the creases in the centre of my palm, or to be held in the crook of my forefinger and stroked by my thumb.

It helps me think.

For as long as I can remember, I've dissected the world into lines, textures, terrains and vanishing points, tracing storylines among the contours. Whether I was balancing my way along tilted sandstone on the beach, seeking banded pebbles in streams, or trailing up a forest track with my parents, every step was layered with questions about how landforms had taken shape. Why was one hill jagged and another smooth? What made the rocks different colours?

I began mapping places out in my head at around the age of nine. Every place had different layers to its map. In its simplest form, my internal map of a specific place highlighted places to play, places to hide, places to run or to paint - or to sit quietly and listen. Then there was another layer, like an acetate overlay, where I would sketch out different rock colours, splits in the minutiae of an area where one rock met another, or where one type of vegetation merged into a second. A third overlay would trace where others had been; by *others* I mean other creatures – birds, animals, insects. This complicated matters for me because birds (and many insects!) fly. I needed to add another dimension to my mapping world. I hadn't yet understood that rocks also twist their way down beneath the earth's surface, but perhaps this was just as well.

My bird map layers were complicated. I remember sitting, baffled, having just watched a sparrowhawk tuck its wings to flip between imperceptible gaps in the trees in our local wood. I found it incredibly difficult to draw its track on to my map. This frustrated me. As a child, bird flight paths had strong rhythms and created intricate, almost melodic woven patterns in my head. The woodland would be threaded together by these wing-trails, like a tapestry.

I read Hugh Miller for the first time three years ago. On a geology trip to the isle of Arran, Angus Miller and I discussed the flickering notion of a geologically-inspired writing competition bearing the great writer's name. On picking up *My Schools and Schoolmasters* I was at once transported back to my own childhood. There was the young Miller, escaping study by heading to the beach, searching for patterns and natural treasure:

> I used to fling myself down on the shore…
> and bethink me, as I passed my fingers
> along the larger grains, of the heaps of gems
> in Aladdin's cavern, or of Sinbad's valley of
> diamonds.

As I read on, I discovered a child thinking in landscape layers and maps, just as I had done. Here was someone who blended the natural world, literature, science, folklore and story, and treated each layer with just as much importance as the next.

For me, Miller's works are as multi-layered as his beloved Old Red Sandstone, and as multi-faceted as the sand crystals held within. Each sentence oozes texture and imagery, and his sense of perspective shifts continually, helping his reader to flip fossil finds – or even cross-sections of bedrock – over and over, twisting them and dissecting them in three-dimensions through words printed on a page.

I began to realise just how feasible a geo-inspired writing competition could be, and that Miller's works would be the ideal source of inspiration to guide the way. As I read further into Miller's own writings and found out more about his life, I began to piece together just how influential he had been. Indeed, his voice has threaded its way throughout the 162 years since his death; both through posthumous publications and through the works and words of other writers, poets, scientists.

Around the same time as I set up the first writing competition in 2015 - which launched on Miller's birthday, the tenth of October - I stumbled across his name in a book called *Landmarks* by Robert Macfarlane. It felt as though Miller was tugging on my sleeve, leading me to follow. In *Landmarks*, Macfarlane credits Miller with giving him 'trilobite sight' – the ability to see backwards into deep time, to envisage creatures that once roamed the Earth, and the landscapes that they would have lived in.

A little over two years later and I'm standing in Macfarlane's study in Cambridge, staring up at a large photographic print of a Scottish sea-stack of sandstone. Along the mantlepiece is a familiar sight: a collection of pebbles and rocks, textures and colours singing.

"I, like Hugh Miller, have a deep affection for sandstones, especially 'Old Red'," says Macfarlane. "When I got my permanent lectureship here twelve years or so ago, I marked it by buying this print of a Scottish sea-stack looming out of mist like the prow of a ship. It keeps a weather eye on me."

Miller was known affectionately by his friends as Old Red, both on account of his shock of red hair and his insightful, ground-breaking work on the vast sandstone deposits across Scotland that bear the same name. Miller's work on the ancient fish fossils found in these stretches of Devonian sandstones – dated around 419 to 360 million years old – is still celebrated today. He spent hours, days, *weeks* painstakingly recreating his beloved armoured fish, scale by scale, bone by bone. His attention to detail is extraordinary, and his beautiful descriptions of the fossils in his many writings continue to inspire. MacFarlane recalls the first time he encountered Miller, and credits him with opening his eyes to the vastness of geological time.

"I was introduced to Hugh Miller while I was a graduate student at Cambridge by my friend Ralph O'Connor, who was then researching the relationship between Romanticism and geology in its early phases," describes Macfarlane. "Like me, Ralph loved Scotland - especially the far north and north-west - and I remember him reading out passages of Miller to me, as one might have read out poems. But of course, they were poems really; rich in metaphor and imagination."

Early geological writing was in its very nature highly speculative. Miller was tentatively envisaging the 'dramas of making' that had gone into this ancient earth. The whole concept of the Earth being older than the Bible proclaimed was still new at this point in history, still raw, and waiting to be fully explored.

"Without doubt I'm inspired most by what I've called the 'deep time spectacles' that Miller slips onto my nose," enthuses Macfarlane. "The sudden seeing-back into the forces and life-forms that have shaped the distant past, and the odd ways in which time, geologically-speaking as well as imaginatively-speaking, isn't simply linear or stratified, but characterised by unconformities and eerie simultaneities that unsteady the ground you walk on."

We head outside, into the grounds of Emmanuel College – "Come and meet a tree," says Macfarlane with an enthusiastic smile. He tells tales of the chalk-spring pond, the trees, their origins – I'm taken with his knowledge of each, what binds them into this place, how they have reached it and become entwined in it.

The tree, by that I mean the one I have been summoned to see, is a superb octopus-armed, many-tentacled Oriental plane tree. Still bare for now, mid-April, there are a few early bluebells under its canopy, soon to become a vivid Van Gogh carpet of blues and greens. I'm beckoned in - you can't help but look up into its vermiculate heart, the branches scribbling the sky. Its many metres across, a semi-circular dome hunched into the ground, like it has landed from outer-space or heaved itself up from the underworld. Macfarlane wonders how long it would be if you laid it out, branch after branch; in my head, we set out on a journey following the unfolded tree through the city, snaking its way to boundaries and out into the Fens beyond. The tree is powerful, alien, holding its sway over and around us, casting its eerie spell.

I discover later that one estimate for the tree's planting date is around 1802, the year of Miller's birth.

Macfarlane, like Miller, is a compulsive walker. He is never still, always tracking boundary lines, fault lines and old ways across the landscape. Both men are 'explorer[s] of caves and ravines... climber[s] among rocks.' Miller's enthusiasm and excitement for what he could find and learn whilst out walking is palpable. His careful, deliberate choice of language and metaphor in describing his fossil finds, particularly in *The Old Red Sandstone*, suggests he is desperate for others to follow in his footsteps, and 'learn to make a right use of your eyes.'

> Creatures whose very type is lost... boat-like animals, furnished with oars and a rudder – fish plated over, like a tortoise, above and below, with a strong armour of bone.

Miller's use of language is often very tactile, using touch and feel to describe his fossil finds and likening their markings to everyday objects. Patternations on his Devonian fish are like flourishes on his aunt's wallpaper, fish scales are roofing tiles pinned on with flooring tacks. The metaphors he uses are often linked to trades, akin to his own early career as a stonemason. He speaks the language of the working men and women of the time, deliberately referring to his own childhood memories of wonder: playing at soldiers with different coloured shell armies on the beach, likening fossils found in rock to currants in a Christmas cake. He pulls people in and helps them relate to his writing.

This detailed focus is another trait that Macfarlane applauds in Miller's work. When I ask him how writers should approach landscape writing - and indeed produce a successful piece for our writing competition in future - he encourages a certain level of obsession and a focus on changes of scale.

"Obsession; because if you stare hard enough at something, or think long enough about it, then it will spring into strangeness again. Changes of scale, because landscape operates at tiny as well as vast levels; the micro-dramas of insect life, soil and rock can be as compelling as the mega-dramas of weather and orogeny. Be a starer into skies, but also be - in the words of Nan Shepherd, who wrote so well about the Cairngorms – 'a peerer into nooks and crannies.'"

Further, Macfarlane adds we should be very wary of cliché in landscape writing: "the sinkholes of cliché are everywhere, ready to swallow up your sentences. If a phrase rises first to your mind, it's probably worth being very suspicious of it, as it's likely to be a cliché, and we've plenty of those in existence in the history of landscape writing, especially about Scotland!"

Just as Miller recreated detail after tiny detail of the fish fossils he found in the Old Red, thereby contributing extensively to the bigger geological picture, so Macfarlane continues in a similar vein in his own work today. He encourages readers back into the realms of trilobite sight and deep time that can be found in our beautiful countryside, and traces the stories of our land and the psychologies these landscapes create.

As I type here several months later, I'm adding another layer to one of my maps in my head. This one traces people, the links between them, their landscapes and their archipelagos of thought. After I met Rob I sent him a piece of bloodstone. He told me it sat on his desk as he finished his next book, *Underland*, which is due out in 2019.

I flip my piece of bloodstone over in the palm of my hand. It quietly sings to me in a tapestry of West Coast island colours, of ancient volcanoes, of deep time.

Learn to Make a Right Use
of Your Eyes

By Jane Verburg

1st Prize in Prose: 2015-16

Fossils are ghosts. Ghosts that I can hold in my hand. Turn in my pocket. Ghosts that last beyond a moment. Fossils stay. They are solid and dependable. Once a nodule is split, it stays split. I can't change the split, can't change the fossil inside. It is. And it will remain.

I have one here. A feathery echo. Filigree tidelines drawn across a sea pebble. Perfect as a hand hold. An anchor to the past. Tonight I use it to weigh open pages. I found it down on the seashore, on the east beach below the midden and the archaeology of medieval Cromarty. I'd like to ask you about it.

Sometimes I sense you about the place. I have walked the Vennels and felt the fringes of your shepherd's plaid brush my arm. I have been at the corner of Church Street at Lammastide and seen you heading off to the Clach Malloch, hammers stuffed into your pockets. Once I saw you and Lydia up in the woods, giggling.

You often saw ghosts threaded through the stairs of time. You said you knew the tilt of old John Feddes wandering in the dark in his light-blue greatcoat. The night your father died you saw a dissevered hand and arm stretch towards you; five years old. Saw straight through where the body should have been to the objects beyond. A ghost. A fleeting fossil. Nothing left for you to hold. Nothing left for you to see and study. No wonder you became fascinated by stony ghosts that stay where they are; caught in their matrix forever.

A fossil is a petrified thing. Once living, now turned to stone. Did you begin to ossify when your father drowned in the man-stealing sea? A few years later, were you gulping for air, calcifying, under your mother's rejection and the death of both your sisters? You wrote that the Accursed Stone, the Clach Malloch, underwent a feverish dream of intense molten heat and overpowering pressure. But how much pressure and sadness can a child contain? How many layers of grief can land on such small shoulders without change? Much later your eldest child died. And more years again, you had a fearful dream the very night you lifted your fisherman's jersey and shot into your skin. Stratification comes in many forms. The delicate layers rot, the scaled harder layers remain and the die is cast. The earth is a book of geological pages and epochs. You were a book. We all are.

At the low point of a spring tide, I climb in to the marble-producing Doocot Cave. A single rock pigeon stays. Here, where bats, like fossils, are locked for winter torpor in crevices and sharp-edged cracks; I rest on the story of a man searching for his wife amongst the mermaids. You too stayed a night here with gasping sea ghosts. So many tales, so many layers. Each of us: a precariously balanced mould with crushed internal features.

In the gloaming a sun-gilt sea outlines the promontory. Curlews etch the crooked bay.

I pace the South Sutor; with fish-bearing Old Red Sandstone and conglomerate below. Could we be formed in some way by the bedrock below us? Could our natures be influenced by the characteristics of the geology in which we live? Could the red sandstones that have been dug from this hillside and that have built my home somehow infuse my very being? You gathered fossil fragments - squashed, contorted jigsaw pieces - collectively revealing the scope and shape of some strange creature. You walked these pathways, followed the contours, knew when a nodule might release another ghost into the world. Did you fear that one day your own father and all the lost souls from your life, would walk, arms out-stretched down the Sutor towards you?

You touched the cold enamel scales of *Osteolepis macrolepidotus*, cracked open from its sea-washed nodule. A story opened, a page in an ancient book, a folktale whispered from the rocks. You: part sennachie, part religious scientist. May be it is not only the Earth that holds deep time and folded complexities but also ourselves.

You call me to observe even the commonest of things. And I try. I watch the seasons kiss the seashore. I know the prevailing winds from the lichen on the rowans and the tilt of the downy birches. Once I touched a dying woodcock when the ground froze through December and into January. I know where the woodpecker raised her young last spring and I watch the treecreepers with their downturned bills skirting ivy-ed ash trees. I hear the chaffinches' warning calls, the wrens alarming my approach, the redshanks as they move ahead of me. I know where the ferns grow greenest and which beech will fall in the next gale and even where the yellow shells get swirled and gather. I collect sea-scoured pebbles with grooves like runes, like Darwin's tree of life; keep them in a basket in the hall. But I do not notice the blue tits' nest and the bull-finches' perch, nor have I plotted the edges of the buzzards' territory. The ex-posed conglomerate by the Target Stone is pointed out to me not observed by me.

I am learning to use my eyes - all my senses - still learning.

Your words stay with me as I take another step along the strandline, as I watch an oystercatcher return, over and over, to her drowned partner.

Updraft

BY PAULA HUNTER

HIGHLY COMMENDED IN PROSE: 2015-16

The summit cairn loomed up out of the bright sky. Molly stepped up to it and spread her fingers across the cool stone. The granite caught the light in slow winks. She turned to look back down the slope and Ross was still out of sight. He might have stopped to take a photo. Probably he'd be trying to catch up, struggling on the scree and cursing her. But if she couldn't see him, the chances were he couldn't see her. She was alone and un-observed as she hadn't been for a long time. She turned her face into the breeze and looked out. At the bottom of the mountain, Loch Leven glimmered like split slate. The walls of Glen Coe swung out of it, up to their silver spines. Beyond them, more mountains tumbled into the haze.

Not far from her feet, the land dropped into a corrie, a giant scoop out of the rock, filled up with air and space. She edged up to the crags and filled her lungs with the warm updraft. It tugged back, gently, like an invitation. It would be easy to accept it, she thought, one little step and whoosh, knowing it was done and could not be undone. There would be time to watch the slide show of her short life with its brittle commentary and feel released.

Time to watch as the staggering walls of granite rushed by and the loch spread below her like a plunge pool. She reached out an arm and felt the force of a wind which had climbed three thousand feet. What a ride that would be.

As she looked out across the void, the air came alive with little lights, swirling and darting. The first time she'd seen them, she'd thought they were raindrops, catching the light as they fell from the sky but their movement was more like a swarm of midges; they had life about them, each one independent of the rest. Yet they'd disappeared under her fingers.

Sparks at the back of her eyes. Just a lack of oxygen, she knew now. But that first time, she'd loved the idea of being able to see inside her head, to see her brain working. She was ten then, staring at the sky outside Mum's, as she waited for Dad, as separate from each of them as they were from each other. The thought sparks had helped her feel less like a foil, as she shuttled between their flats, reflecting back at each of them what they wanted to see, missing someone always.

Up in the mountains, she didn't miss anyone. From where she stood, there wasn't a single human visible. The crust of the earth was folded, wrought into peaks and ridges, lit by the vast sky. Everything was light and possibility. There was room to breathe and think.

In a couple of weeks, she was supposed to be going back to uni. Final year, law. Her classmates were writing for the law journals, chasing traineeships, hungry for the future, as she should be. It was the age of connectivity. There were democratic revolutions happening all over the world and more than ever, people could work together for justice. There was everything to live for, everything to fight for. But the bad news resonated more, the brutality of oppressive regimes, the suffocation of peaceful protest, and closer to home, the victimisation of the poor. The people who most needed lawyers couldn't afford them. The only firms hiring trainees were the ones representing the vested interests which were screwing up democracy. When she'd asked about this at the jobs fair, one of her classmates had dug her in the ribs. "You don't bite the hand that feeds, Molls."

For a while, she'd thought direct political action was the way to go and joined the Occupy group at uni. But then Ross let it slip at a meeting that her mum was advising the Department for Work and Pensions. Some of the members were okay about it but most started looking at her differently. By the summer, it had become more his thing than hers. And generally these days, she felt sort of invisible. People stopped talking when she joined the conversation, narrowed their eyes and turned away. It was strange and confusing.

She caught herself glancing in shop windows, to check she was still there. The reflections showed her but not her, face pinched, eyes muddy in dark hollows, the brown hair in dreadlocks which had formed over the summer without her consent. Ross liked them. But even Ross was colder to her lately. She didn't really blame him. The delusions she'd been having about him were every day now, the nights broken by dreams. Worst of all was the weight over her head, pressing down around her ears and making her slow. Like a lid. She didn't know herself.

And now she was at the top of a mountain again. It felt surreal, in a good way. She'd thought she'd given up climbing. But no one had told Jess, Max and Pete. They'd pestered her to come with them, even though she'd ducked their messages and calls for months. Pete had even come round to the flat to talk her into it. And he'd answered all Ross's questions, calmly smiling through the sarcasm. Max's dad had a gap in the holiday lets and was happy to let them have the cottage in Onich for the week, so long as they didn't wreck it. The gas bottles needed replacing and a few other jobs which they could do to pay their way. He'd borrowed a van and equipment from the Mountaineering Club. All she needed was beer money. It left Ross with nothing to object to and her, more grateful than afraid.

The breeze swirled around her, holding her up, as ripped clouds moved across the sun and the light changed from grey to brilliant white and back again.

Old is Tomorrow

BY JIM MACKINTOSH

JOINT 3RD PRIZE IN POETRY: 2015-16

You can see it clearly, if you allow yourself, to pause, to
breathe out
for the briefest of moments away from the grub
that befuddles our imagination, the digital bleed of
information.

life itself is a school
and Nature
always a fresh study

layers of past generations
mulch of past millenniums
the openings, the chasms
the marks of ancient furrows

successive soils laid bare in stratified gravel, moraines
of memory unpicked
by him, to be scooped up, understood - learning
the memorial of time, a clock ticking past our fragile
existence barely
a thin layer of history visible, relevant – brushed
by the frequent eddy of tides where humanity shifted

along the shore
and in that shallow glimpse of our past, man
emptied his mouth of gravel and found the plough to
till his story

and that the man
who keeps his eyes
and his mind open
will always find fitting

How long have we stumbled and understood nothing?
Not him.
He walked with a steady pace: noticed the difference,
even a section of a few feet, our two lines of pointless
text message lost
where in that time, he would find an archipelago
of islands, brushed by frequent icebergs, and the lift of
creatures
sub-arctic molluscs, sand floods, a belief
in all that's left under our feet, belongs in our minds, in
our imaginations

though it may be
hard school masters
to speed him
on his lifelong education

I am sure of this – Hugh Miller's stride was unbroken,
in seeing our story.
His footprints apparent today in the unravelling
of our tomorrows, the unfurling coil of our layers, the
unlocking of ourselves
to place fresh words on the shelf next to his.

Footnote: The words in italics are the last four lines from Hugh Miller's book,
My Schools and Schoolmasters, Edinburgh, 1993.

Voyaging with Hugh Miller

By Simon Cuthbert with Joyce Gilbert

My mobile phone buzzed from somewhere in the bottom of my rucksack. I was dozing in a wicker chair in the bread-oven heat of a beach cabin in Sri Lanka. I fumbled to find it, half-asleep, surprised to see it working after two weeks without a signal. It was a text message from Joyce Gilbert, the education officer for the Royal Scottish Geographical Society (RSGS). I was immediately swept back a few weeks to cool, misty mornings in the central Scottish Highlands, the straps of a heavy pack biting into my shoulders, trekking along the old Thieves' Road from Dalwhinnie to Fort William. Joyce, in collaboration with a splendid little educational charity called the SpeyGrian Trust, had organised the journey – the Bedrock Walk – bringing together a unique party of artists, writers, dramatists, educators, an eco-tourism specialist, and me (a geologist). The Walk came out of a project called 'Stories in the Land' that encouraged young people to engage with the Scottish landscape and its profound connections with their culture. We walked, talked and shared our different perspectives and insights about Highland landscape and culture, and the influence of its rocky foundations. Each of us experienced the rigours of the physical journey, the form and texture of the scenery and the stuff of the ground itself, but we also made a journey of the imagination that nourished our creativity. We might craft creation stories, find ways to transmute the mountains into our own favoured medium or let the landscape become the matrix for a human story. Each of us emerged from the wildlands enriched with new ways to look at mountains. All of us emerged from the journey with our own, and our collective stories from the wildlands we had crossed.

Joyce's text message suggested that we try another geological journey, but this time by sea, in a traditional sailing ship through the Small Isles. Here's how she remembers our initial exchange on the matter:

It all began with a mobile phone conversation in the unlikeliest of places. I was on board the old sailing boat Leader *off the remote west coast of Scotland and Simon (I discovered later) was on Sri Lanka. I was so excited by the geology while anchored off Jura, that I texted Simon to suggest we should plan some sort of geological project to follow on from the Bedrock Walk I'd organised the previous year. However, instead of travelling on land, I thought we could take a journey by sea – the 'Bedrock Boat', I suggested? Simon immediately replied: "Ahhh, that would be Hugh Miller and* Cruise of the Betsey." *We both had very fleeting mobile reception, so I wasn't able to discover more until I returned to port a few days later. What was Simon was talking about? When I got back to the RSGS office, I was able to do some detailed research and arranged to meet Martin Gostwick from the charity The Friends of Hugh Miller. Leakey's second-hand bookshop in Inverness housed many old copies of Hugh's publications and was the perfect place to have lunch to discuss how to take the project forward. Martin talked with passion and knowledge about Hugh Miller and it soon became clear that* The Cruise of the Betsey *was a wonderful story about an amazing journey. Furthermore, I realised that a remarkable polymath had largely been forgotten in Scotland and this needed to be addressed – I was hooked!*

I first found Hugh Miller gathering dust on a library shelf in the foxed pages of *The Old Red Sandstone*. I was looking for something else, but the name halted my scan along the rows of books because I'd spent the previous few years immersed in the Old Red rocks of Norway and Scotland. I knew nothing of the author. Opening it at the first chapter it was odd to find a geology text starting with a moral sermon urging the Victorian values of hard work and self-improvement, but somehow his archaic language and heroically long sentences held me with the pictures he painted. He had a way of connecting obscure or complicated ideas to homely, everyday experiences that took you along with him ('ah, yes, I see it now...'). It soon became clear that his origins were humble, yet he had a hungry intellect and a boldness that drove him to challenge the views of those in influential positions – men he admired for their talent, and others he loathed for their abuse of power. *The Old Red Sandstone* was conceived as the work of an amateur geologist who wished to better establish the status of strata that he knew intimately, as an artisan who had wrought them as a stonemason and as a uniquely observant and perceptive investigator; he aspired to persuade the patricians of the science of its true significance. Yet, at the same time, he would open its wonders to the mind of his most 'humble' reader.

Geology, like astronomy and archaeology, remains to this day an endeavour in which anyone can contribute, even without a formal education in the subject. In Scotland, this explains the continuing success of local geological societies. As Miller said in *The Old Red Sandstone*, 'it cannot be too extensively known, that nature is vast and knowledge limited, and that no individual, however humble in place or acquirement, need despair of adding to the general fund.' Yet geology itself has a role in shaping the imagination beyond its formal scientific realm. A few pages on, Miller says 'Geology, of all the sciences, addresses itself most powerfully to the imagination.' At the most profound level it has shaped our modern minds to accept enormous spans of time as a self-evident truth and has lent its concepts to everyday language and ideas with shifting tectonic plates and global catastrophes. But geology is also woven into the fabric of our culture and imagination in the form of landscapes, the texture and tactility of raw materials and its evidence and inspiration for creation stories. It was this fabric that we explored in the Bedrock Walk, but Hugh Miller gave us the inspiration to take our Stories in the Land onto the seaways, and to a wider audience.

The Cruise of the Betsey or, a Summer Ramble Among the Fossiliferous Deposits of the Hebrides is a classic of Scottish travel literature and a delight to read. Miller takes a holiday from his demanding work as a newspaper editor in Edinburgh, joining his old school friend the Rev. John Swanson for a voyage through the Small Isles in a leaky old pleasure yacht, *Betsey*, that has become a floating manse for the new Free Church. Swanson would minister to his flock and Miller would head off with his hammer, chisels and shoulder bag to explore the geology. His title leads his reader to expect this, but there is so much more. He was a celebrity among the followers of the Free Church. His pen, which had challenged the heresies of Lamark on evolution, had also been a weapon with far greater social impact in the schism of the Kirk, a seismic upheaval in Scottish life - a social and religious revolt against patronage that led to the formation of the

Free Church. In *Betsey* we find a deep empathy with the people of the Small Isles and a fascination with their history and folklore that slips seamlessly into his boundless curiosity with the foundations of the land – volcanic convulsions, singing sands, Oolitic life. Among geologists, Hugh Miller is still famous for his discovery of marine reptile fossils on the Isle of Eigg and for his vivid reconstruction of the forest of *Pinites eiggensis* in a Tertiary-age valley and its violent destruction by a volcanic eruption.

We followed the *Betsey* for part of its cruise, thankfully in a more seaworthy vessel. *Leader* is a one-hundred-year-old Brixham trawler of nineteen berths, one-hundred and ten feet from stem to stern. In September 2014, at the North Pier in Oban the skipper and professional crew were joined by a motley one of writers, artists, broadcasters, musicians, traditional storytellers, a geologist, a geographer – and Joyce, who had the unique imagination and vision to bring such a diverse and creative group together. We had also recruited three young, aspiring geologists to show them some world-class geology and a hundred new ways to imagine it. The focus of the voyage was Eigg, where much of *The Cruise of the Betsey* was set. Glimmers of memory from this journey still flicker into my consciousness to make me smile at unexpected moments; following Hugh up the gully on An Sgùrr (a glass mountain!) past fantastical pitchstone columns like 'the erections of some old gigantic race passed from the Earth for ever' and that 'belly over with a curve, like the ribs of some wrecked vessel from which the planking had been torn away'; wide-eyed children in Eigg school listening to traditional stories; the story of the Eigg islanders' community buy-out, a modern-day schism from patronage; a pod of dolphins riding our bow-wave – inheritors of the ichthyosaur lifestyle; music, stories and dancing on the deck on moonlit

Loch Sunart. For Joyce, a seasoned voyager in traditional sailing craft among the Hebrides, it gave a new and
deeply rewarding perspective:

*I had visited Eigg many times and thought I knew the island
and the people quite well. However, following Hugh's journey
allowed me to gain many new and unexpected perspectives
on the island's history and on our relationship with the land.
Simon captured it perfectly when he commented that the old
sailing boat* Leader *was like a time-machine which allowed
us to move through space and time. An added richness came
from our interdisciplinary group aged seventeen to seventy.
However, for me the most significant thing was combining
the retracing of the journey with reading passages from* The
Cruise of the Betsey. *How strange and magical it was to
anchor our boat in the same spot as Hugh had done 170 years
ago, while reading and reflecting on how it was for him. It was
just possible to imagine we had been transported to another
time and another world.*

A second voyage with *Leader* followed a year later that
we called 'Testimony of the Rocks: Journeys through
time' after another of Miller's books. *Testimony* is not
for the faint hearted – a densely argued text setting out
Miller's thesis on creation in which he attempts to rec-
oncile his deep knowledge of palaeontology with his
evangelical Christian convictions. In spite of this, we
took his title and his basic idea of past 'creations', long
extinct, and combined it with our experience from the
year before of a vessel and its crew moving through
deep time as seen through the rocks and the lens of our
different imaginations. This time we cruised through
the Atlantic islands off Argyll, our route dictated by the
tides and winds and the traditional capabilities of *Leader*.
Argyll embodies the interwoven threads in the fabric of

a landscape - geology, topography, culture and history. Its long fingers of land, defined by the negative image of its fjords, are a sculpture fashioned by the Pleistocene ice-sheet working on a Dalradian mille-feuille of harder and softer strata, thrown into contortions by ancient collisions of continents. The sea-lochs and sounds have shaped the sea-routes of migrations and trade between Scotland and Ireland over thousands of years, with profound cultural consequences. We saw this especially in the Garvellach Islands, a fin of hard conglomerate erupting out of the Firth of Lorne, a rough place of contemplation for St Brendan and his followers and, possibly, the grave of St Columba's mother. Yet the Garvellachs tell of an almost unimaginably older and stranger world where icebergs crammed the tropical oceans.

Each day, *Leader* delivered us to a new landing place, where our explorations and conversations might roam over stone tools in Mesolithic shell-middens, a lime kiln, Irish saints, medieval architecture, botany, George Orwell, and the origins of musical instruments (a pebble with a hole). Yet, the testimony of the rocks in the Atlantic islands arising from modern science tells a story stranger than the wildest tale from folklore: a frozen Earth in a far earlier eon; a deathly blue-white globe, rescued from eternal, frigid sleep by the hot, foetid breath of volcanoes. As on the first voyage with Hugh Miller, we wished to share our experiences and the inspiration that Hugh Miller had sparked within us with other communities, an aspiration that Joyce had striven to fulfil:

I wanted to finish our second Miller-inspired voyage at the island of Luing, one of the Slate Islands that had roofed the world in the nineteenth and twentieth centuries. Leader *arrived in time for us to join the Luing community in inaugurating the newly-build Atlantic Islands Centre, celebrating the region's natural history and industrial legacy.* Leader's *crew told the story of its journey in pictures, charts and song and the Luing folk told their stories and gave us their poetry and music. It may be the only ceilidh ever to have included a geology lesson! I felt sure Hugh would have approved.*

The two Hugh Miller-inspired voyages have given inspirational experiences for their crews, especially for the young geologists sponsored to join them. But there is a wider legacy. The *Betsey* voyage was linked to a Hugh Miller festival on the Isle of Eigg and events for schools in Edinburgh and the Black Isle. Later that month The Friends of Hugh Miller, who sponsored both voyages, hosted the We Are Cromarty festival in the town of Miller's birth. The two Hebridean voyages benefitted from collaboration between The Friends of Hugh Miller and the Scottish Geodiversity Forum, and this has continued with the two Hugh Miller Writing Competitions. The fruits of this collaboration lie in these pages – a testimony to the power of geology to nourish and inspire the imagination and deepen our connection with the Earth, and with each other.

Pterichthyodes milleri

BY MICHAEL DAVENPORT

JOINT 3RD PRIZE IN POETRY: 2015-16

A specimen sits in glass-cased silence.
But I hear the clink, clink of his hammer and chisel,
clear like a stonechat in the morning air.
Miller, in his search for fossils,
an explorer of ravines, loiterer along sea-shores,
climber among rocks, labourer in quarries.

He splits a nodule to reveal the first example
of a 'winged-fish' from the Old Red Sandstone.
I opened it with a single blow and there lay the effigy
of a creature, fashioned out of jet, two 'arms' articulated
at the shoulders, head lost in the trunk, long angular tail.
Its armoured plates remind him of a turtle.

In *My Schools and Schoolmasters* he describes
his life in Cromarty, family history, education,
work as a stonemason, fascination with geology.
To Miller fossils were *Footprints of the Creator*
that he reproduced in detailed diagrams.
He believed in successive creations by the deity.

A Cromarty churchyard: cold echoes of his trade.
Miller carves the headstone of his child, Eliza.
The last time he ever put chisel on stone, his wife reported*.
Years later, different reverberations:
alone at home he shoots himself.
Despair from religious doubt? Fear of brain disease?

The National Museum: *Beginnings, Life in the
Mid-Devonian*.
A sandstone slab, small fish fossil secretive through rise
and fall
of species, mass extinctions, the appearance of reptiles,
mammals, advent of *Homo sapiens* - until released by
Miller.
I focus on the label *Pterichthyodes milleri* and see a
symbiosis,
two existences confirmed by the power of naming.

Eons between the lives joined in this binomial.
I whisper *Pterichthyodes milleri*, a 'winged-fish'
swims in warm seas and Miller moves clear
of tragedies and struggles. He's part of a community
of discovery and the mystery of how, through transient
beings,
the world begins to comprehend itself.

* Sutherland, E. Article in *Celebrating the Life and Times of Hugh Miller*, Edited
by Borley, L. Cromarty Arts Trust, Edinburgh (2003)

Written in Stone:
Geology and Graffiti in Orkney

BY ANTONIA THOMAS

2ND PRIZE IN PROSE: 2015-16

Orkney's story has always been written in stone. Underneath its rich soil lie thick layers of Devonian flagstone, laid down as sediments when the islands were submerged under Lake Orcadie millions of years ago. The ghosts of old sun-cracks and wave ripples are often visible in the strata, along with the fossilised remains of ancient fish: the ichthyolites of the famous Sandwick Fish Bed. These lake deposits helped form the rolling landscape of Orkney today; soft hills giving way to sea-cliffs, indented by deep geos along lithic flaws in the readily-fractured flagstone. Its properties have been exploited from the earliest times, quarried for walling stone and roof-slates from the Neolithic to the present day.

Old extraction scars punctuate the landscape. On the edge of the west coast just outside Stromness lie the remains of the Black Craig quarry, opened in the 1770s to satisfy the exploding population's demand for building stone. Slates were loaded straight onto boats and transported to customers throughout Scotland. Within twenty years, it was producing some thirty to forty thousand slates annually, and they were considered the best available. But this boom industry was not to last. By the early nineteenth century, they were not worthy of export, and in the Ordnance Survey map of the 1880s, the quarry lies unmarked. It was not, however, forgotten.

Known as an excellent site for ichthyolites from at least the 1830s, Professor T.S. Traill of the University of Edinburgh collected fossils from the area, corresponding with Louis Agassiz and sending him drawings and maps. Orkney's west coast was, Hugh Miller exclaimed, a 'Land of Fish'. At the height of the Black Craig's slate industry, Miller was still a quarrier, yet to discover the fossil fish that dominated his life. But in 1846, by now a renowned geologist, he travelled to Orkney to see the Old Red Sandstone and the fossil fish sandwiched in its ancient layers.

By the time of Miller's visit, the Black Craig quarry was no longer worked, its spoil tips explored by fossil hunters rather than stonemasons. No accounts survive of the men who once worked the slates. But in the geo just downslope of the quarry, where they would eat their lunch shielded from the wind, they left a different record. Whether because the need to work stone was so ingrained in their daily life, or perhaps because they just had to make their mark, those quarrymen carved their names, and sometimes dates, on the geo's flagstone walls.

Those who visit the site today are surprised by the palimpsest. The soft flagstone is vulnerable to the elements and many of the earliest dates have been eroded, replaced by new inscriptions or suffocated by encroaching black lichen. A generation ago many more carvings dating from the late eighteenth century were visible; local names – Mowat, Linklater, Cursiter, Budge – mingling with less familiar ones. There are hundreds of names and dates now, ranging from the 1770s when the quarry was opened right up to the present day. Most, however, are from the mid to late nineteenth century: declarations of identity in a new age of literacy and leisure.

By that time, tourists had become a familiar sight along the west coast, fossil hunting amongst the spoil of the old quarry, carving their names and taking lunch in the sheltered geo. Promoted by writers such as Miller, geology had become an exciting and fashionable new hobby, whilst a generation of Victorians had grown up with the work of Walter Scott romanticising the Highlands and Islands to tourists. Scott had visited Orkney in 1814 on a six-week summer cruise with the Northern Lighthouse Board collecting folk-tales. Many were later integrated into *The Pirate* (1822), but one stands out in particular: the Dwarfie Stone. A massive block of Old Red, it is one of several in a remote valley at the north end of Hoy, but unlike the others, it has been hollowed out forming a small chamber. Presumed to be a Neolithic tomb, it was immortalised in *The Pirate* as the home of the dwarf, Trollid.

A generation later, during his own summer cruise to Orkney, Hugh Miller visited the infamous Dwarfie Stone. With his stonemason's eye he found a 'compact' stone that he estimated he could carve out to order in a matter of weeks. But as was often the case with Miller, what intrigued him was not just its geological properties, but the human story it told. Inside the tomb he found numerous graffiti, including the inscriptions of H. Ross 1735, and P. Folster 1830. And just as quarrymen and tourists had felt compelled to do in the geo below Black Craig, Miller also felt moved to leave his mark, as he describes in *Rambles of a Geologist*:

> The rain still pattered heavily overhead;
> and with my geological chisel and hammer
> I did, to beguile the time, what I very rarely

do,—added my name to the others…which, if both they and the Dwarfie Stone get but fair play, will be distinctly legible two centuries hence. In what state will the world then exist, or what sort of ideas will fill the head of the man who, when the rock has well-nigh yielded up its charge, will decipher the name for the last time, and inquire, mayhap, regarding the individual whom it now designates, as I did this morning, when I asked, "Who was this H. Ross, and who this P. Folster?".

His words were rendered all the more poignant by their posthumous publication. On Christmas Day 1856, Hugh Miller shot himself dead. But the legacy of his writing engaged an entire generation, contributing to the new era of popular science which would come to define the nineteenth century. His story too had been written in stone: firstly as a quarryman, latterly as a geologist. It is fitting that his name lives on in Orkney, 'distinctly legible two centuries hence', written into the very fabric of the Devonian sandstone that defined his work and life.

Hugh Miller's Palace of Printing

By Michael Taylor

As a teenager I discovered Hugh Miller in the form of my great-uncle's cheap copy of Miller's autobiography *My Schools and Schoolmasters* in the family bookcase. In this book is a blurry photograph captioned 'The "Witness" Office, Edinburgh' (Figure 1). This referred to the Edinburgh newspaper which Miller edited from 1840 to his death. The photograph was obviously taken in a run-down part of Edinburgh's Old Town, but I could place it no further and left it at that until, decades later, I came to work at National Museums Scotland, which holds most of Miller's geological collection. I started researching his life, and found that the editorial office of *The Witness* was in the High Street opposite the High Kirk of St Giles, as marked by the present-day plaque on the City Chambers. This was plainly not the street in the photograph. However, *The Witness* also had a 'printing office' – as printing workshops were then called – close by in Horse Wynd, now part of Guthrie Street (Figure 2). Here *The Witness* was printed from 1840 to 1864, and here, too, many editions of Miller's books were printed until about 1870. Further research into accounts of Miller's life, and Ordnance Survey maps, trade directories, rates valuations, local newspapers, sasines, and other archives, confirms that the printing office was indeed in the building in the photograph and its next-door neighbour, not visible there. However, the story is complex and the evidence patchy, and it's not always clear precisely what was happening when and where. This research, to be published in full elsewhere, also throws new light on Miller's business relationships. As this essay shows, I also gained a better feel for the physical side of Miller's life and work in the context of the Edinburgh of his time, with people and industry on top of each other.

The printing office was partly in a rented 1730s grand house, visible in the mystery photo. Built by the eminent Edinburgh physician John Clerk, it was the northernmost of three upper-class town houses on the west side of Horse Wynd, interspersed with what were surely their former coach-houses and service buildings (Figure 3). Behind this row of grand houses was a fourth, Minto House, set in its grounds (the University of Edinburgh's modern building of that name is almost on the same site). This Horse Wynd (there are others in the old burghs of Edinburgh, Canongate and Leith) had indeed been an upmarket street, part of the main route from the south via Potterrow which dived into the Cowgate and then climbed up to the High Street in the days before the Bridges were built. However, during the eighteenth and early nineteenth centuries, Edinburgh's gentry and professional families fled to the New Town and the southern suburbs. Like so many other Old Town mansions, those in Horse Wynd lost their prestigious occupants, and were subdivided into workshops and low-grade 'houses', with shop windows and doors knocked through the ground floor façades.

Figure 1. The lower part of Guthrie Street (formerly Horse Wynd) at its junction with the Cowgate, from a Collins edition of *My Schools and Schoolmasters* published around 1907 (Miller undated). Hugh Miller's newspaper and printing firm were based partly in the former grand town house on the left as seen here. The image is datable to 1895-1906 from the shop signs in the photo, including Siger the German baker on the left at No. 16 - who let the whole rear ground floor (his ovens were still there in 1928). There was also Meyer the cabinetmaker upstairs at No. 14 (through the original central doorway, with the top-hatted gentleman). The printing operation may also, at one time, have used the little shop behind and to the right of the pedlar with basket.

Figure 2. Then and now: nearly the same view in 2016. The pale-toned hotel in the centre occupies the site of the buildings in Figure 1, replacing the cask store built by the neighbouring brewery after the demolition of the old house in 1928. The stone tenement to its left was built by Miller's former partner, Fairly, in about 1875 on the site of another building which the firm had used, probably for their steam printing press. His application for permission in the Edinburgh City Archives shows that the new doorway visible here opened onto a through-passage. This gave direct access to the new printing work-shop which the firm built after Miller's death, in the backyard of the old grand house next door. Photograph by M. A. Taylor.

The other building which the firm rented, next door to the big house, was a former gateway to Minto House, its arched double-doored entrance giving way to a through-passage flanked by rooms on either side and with a flat above. In 1928, Clerk's house was described in *The Scotsman* by W. Forbes Gray (who misidentified it as the neighbouring Earl of Galloway's House):

> It was an elegant and admirably proportioned house of several storeys, deeper behind than in front, and facing east and west. There was an imposing façade surmounted by a pediment with urns [...] The central portion of the mansion projected slightly from the wings, and the handsome doorway was reached by a few steps. The entrance hall was paved with marble, while the staircase had hand-wrought wooden railings of a high standard of craftsmanship. Altogether [the] House wore an aspect of magnificence even in its degenerate days.

I was astonished to find, in the City Archives, a complete set of plans of Clerk's building, dated 1928. They even showed a baker's two large ovens in the back corner of the large ground floor back room, resting directly on the subsoil. At first I assumed that the ovens had been built on the footings of the steam-powered press. But given the inconvenient access up steps, it is far more likely that this building was used for lighter work such as typesetting, administration and storage, and that the steam engine and press were in the former gatehouse next door. A little demolition of the passageway walls would open up a large space on ground level. There was already vehicular access on this level in the front yard

Figure 3. An evocative photographic record of the area of Horse Wynd was made by Archibald Burns just as slum clearance was beginning in late 1870. This is Burns' photograph of the Earl of Galloway's House halfway down Horse Wynd, when demolition in the area had already started, and most properties had been vacated. Note the similar grand house visible downhill, also with a projecting gable end bearing bases for urns on the pediment. Miller's printing office was in this building, and in another between it and Galloway's, set back from the street and visible here only as the low stone wall and iron railings of its front yard. Historic Environment Scotland image DP 242224 © courtesy of HES (W. and R. Chambers Collection).

and possibly even through to the back yard, for heavy deliveries such as coal. Where one would expect printers to be going to and fro, the Ordnance Survey map of 1852 shows a gap cut in the side wall of the backyard to give access to the big house.

In 1840, steam printing was so costly as to be justified only when a lot of work had to be done quickly, more quickly than hand-operated printing presses could cope with: as, indeed, when a newspaper had thousands of copies to get printed and off to its readers the same night. Evidently John Johnstone and Robert Fairly, the original publishers of *The Witness*, had serious plans for their new newspaper when they had this machinery installed right from the start. I don't know whether the steam engine itself, its boiler, or both, were in the main part of the gatehouse building, or in a projecting structure in the yard – the latter is visible on the large-scale Ordnance Survey map. The upper rooms and the big house would have been useful for other work when not let to other users. The open backyards would have given at least some daylight for the printers, depending on how high the brewery behind was. Just south of the brewery, behind the Horse Wynd properties, were driveways (and presumably gardens) surrounding a Baptist chapel and Minto House, then a hospital.

This location makes sense, in that it was only a short scamper up Old Fishmarket Close to the editorial office in the High Street and back, for a printer's apprentice carrying copy and proofs. And when the newspapers had to be despatched expeditiously, they did not have to be taken far to the railway terminals on the site of the modern Waverley Station, or the Post Office, near the north end of North Bridge. It does seem odd to modern eyes to place an industrial steam engine in a ground-floor workshop at the bottom of a steep valley surrounded in part by high-rise tenement housing, however well-ventilated this might be by Edinburgh's vicious crosswinds. But that was normal then; the engine would have had no more power than an ordinary industrial electric motor today. Much larger steam printing works could be found in central Edinburgh, such as those of W. & R. Chambers located just north of the High Kirk of St Giles.

The firm of Johnstone & Fairly printed and published *The Witness* at these two offices. The newspaper and its editor Miller were crucial in developing the support for what was then called the Evangelical wing of the Church of Scotland which formed the new Free Church in the Disruption of 1843. The next year, in 1844, Miller bought out Johnstone's share, which had been held on behalf of a group of prominent Evangelicals who provided the original financial backing for the newspaper. This created the firm of Miller & Fairly, who printed some of Miller's books for John Johnstone and other publishers. After Miller's death in 1856, his widow Lydia held his share in the partnership on behalf of his family. The firm acquired the two main Horse Wynd buildings, and even erected a new printing workshop in the back yard of the big house, but the newspaper soon closed, in 1864. Robert Fairly then bought out the family and continued the printing business with their old foreman William Lyall. Fairly retired in 1866, leasing the printing workshop to one Robert Sanson. Sanson's departure, around 1871, finally ended the printing of Miller's writings on this site, so far as we know. A possible reason for his removal was the noise and dirt from the demolition of almost every building in the Wynd, including the former Minto House gateway (Figure 4). This was during one of the improvement schemes pushed through by William Chambers, Lord Provost. This clearance made space for the new, and eponymous, Chambers Street. It certainly made a fine setting for the University, Watt Institution and School of Arts (later Heriot-Watt College), and the Edinburgh Museum of Science and Art, which had acquired most of Miller's geological collection in 1859. This 'educational boulevard', as architectural historian Charles McKean called it (McKean 2000: 130), is still ornamented by the statue of Chambers, whose brother Robert was the anonymous author of the transmutationist *Vestiges of the Natural History of Creation* of 1844 – a proto-evolutionary work attacked by Hugh Miller amongst others.

One wonders about the impact of Horse Wynd on Miller. Having his own books printed in his own works raises interesting questions about Miller's bargaining ability with his publisher, as well as his working practices as a writer (though he did not publish that many complete books during his life, as some of his books were posthumous assemblages from articles and pamphlets). More generally, Fairly was an efficient printer and manager, greatly appreciated by Miller. Nevertheless, editing a newspaper twice weekly, week in, week out, was a huge strain that ultimately told on Miller's health, already weakened by lung disease from his days as a stonemason. Co-owning the paper must have made it that much harder for him to contemplate escaping by resigning his position.

There was, however, some light relief. Miller provided simple gymnastics for his printers in the backyard, including traditional Scottish stone putting, which Miller always won – except when they were joined by an employee of the brewery over the back wall, a champion at heavy Highland sports. There is a nice story of Miller competing with two friends, the prominent Free Church ministers Thomas Guthrie and Thomas McCrie the younger, to make a standing jump from the floor

Figure 4. Burns took this picture standing in West College Street, looking northwards. The only building recognisable today, just visible in the left foreground, is the extreme north-eastern corner of the Edinburgh Museum of Science and Art. Horse Wynd dives down to the Cowgate in the distance, past the boxy Gaelic Chapel and the first two grand houses on the left. North College Street, complete with relocation placards and posters, runs across this view in the middle ground. It would soon be massively widened over Horse Wynd to create Chambers Street: hence today's sudden descent by stairs to what remains of the Wynd at the bottom of Guthrie Street. Historic Environment Scotland image DP 242226 © courtesy of HES (W. and R. Chambers Collection).

onto the editor's desk. Miller won, at the cost of splitting the desk in two. This was perhaps in the editorial office rather than the printing office. But it was certainly in Horse Wynd that William Cunningham, latterly Professor of Theology at the Free Church College, made evening visits to deal with the proofs of his articles in *The Witness*. One of his biographers, Miller's former assistant James Mackenzie, recalled cheerful times over coffee on the twice-weekly 'publishing nights, when we manufactured it in our gigantic coffee-pot – Hugh Miller, meanwhile, contriving to toast cheese by the help of the fire-shovel' (Rainy and Mackenzie 1871: 138).

As for the area around the printing office, the Cowgate was a sump of poverty, misery, and disease. Cunningham's biographers recalled Horse Wynd as a 'region squalid beyond all telling' (Rainy and Mackenzie 1871: 137). Guthrie, founder of the Ragged Schools for poor children, did much pastoral work in this area, 'with a few exceptions, occupied by the lowest, poorest and most degraded people' (Guthrie and Guthrie 1874: I: 196; the reworked and diverted Horse Wynd was presumably renamed Guthrie Street for him). Charles McKean suggested that the ghastly sights helped drive some of Miller's most potent writing (McKean 2002). Miller surely had the area in mind when he visited Rùm in 1844 during the cruise of the *Betsey* and wondered why the Highlanders had to be cleared off their land where they could make a living, when – Miller implied – there were many better candidates for emigration 'in our workhouses, – more than enough on our pauper-rolls, – more than enough huddled up, disreputable, useless, and unhappy, in the miasmatic alleys and typhoid courts of our large towns' (Miller 1858: 135). He went on to argue in his 1854 article 'Our working classes', reprinted in *Essays* (Miller 1862: 146-147), that

> [...] society has failed. It is idle to speak of sanitary reform, and almost idle to speak of moral reform, when we contemplate the dwellings of a large portion of the working population. We can no more expect propriety of conduct in the individual if we clothe him in rags, and keep him in rags, than we can expect propriety of conduct in a family that lives habitually in the wretched lodgments which disgrace our towns and cities.

It is no coincidence that Miller has a street named for him in the Colonies development of Stockbridge, built by the self-help artisan housing movement of the later nineteenth century.

The grand house in Horse Wynd survived into the twentieth century with an assortment of tenants. The upper floors were occupied in 1907 by the Scottish Navvy Mission Society, rather appropriately in view of Miller's years as an itinerant stonemason. The 1928 plans show what looks like an attic dormitory for men travelling through from one job to another, with neat rows of skylights inserted into the roof and a couple of lavatory cubicles in the corner. Those plans, however, were drawn for the neighbouring brewery's successful application for permission to demolish the building. How sad! Just as his birthplace cottage in Cromarty is a rare survivor of its time, Hugh Miller's palace of printing would have been a precious architectural treasure in a modern urban landscape dominated by Victorian pastiche and twentieth century harling.

Data from Edinburgh Council Archives, National Records of

Scotland and National Library of Scotland. I am grateful to their staff and those of Historic Environment Scotland and the libraries of National Museums Scotland and the University of Leicester.

A Different Kind of Light

By Kenneth Steven

2ND PRIZE IN POETRY: 2015-16

To climb out of the known
into the moorland's empty miles;
where sun and shadow meet
and the only elements the ones
that first began this world:
wind and water, rock and light.

You crouch beside the loch,
out of the bullying of the breeze –
and nothing might have changed
since the beginning;
a smear of brightness smiles the water,
before going back to grey.

Somewhere unseen the sadness of a bird –
a single song in the hugeness of the sky,
and suddenly you know you do not matter
here beyond the normal and the everyday,
the old enslavement of the hours –

you have escaped to breathe
a different kind of light.

Caolas

Meòrachadh air Caolas na Linne Duibhe, dòchas-siubhail, agus cothroman an taobh thall. No bhos.

BY MÀIRI ANNA NICUALRAIG (MARY ANN KENNEDY)

HIGHLY COMMENDED IN PROSE: 2015-16

(Chaidh an aiste seo a sgrìobhadh bho thùs anns a' Ghàidhlig, agus tha i air a tabhann mar thagradh Ghàidhlig. Tha eadar-theangachadh Beurla gu h-ìosal.)

Sheas mi.

Sheas mi air bruaichean na linne, a' coimhead a-null gu dùthaich nach b' aithne dhomh, ach san dol-seachad. An dol-seachad, gach bliadhna, gach turas a bhiomaid a' deanamh air an Eilean. Air tighinn tarsainn Loch Lìobhann 's na carbadan a' cur nan caran ann am bhalsa na h-aiseige bige sin. A' leantainn oirnn gu tuath. Mise an còmhnaidh a' gabhail ionghnaidh bhon chùl: saoil dè an t-àite mìorbhaileach, annasach a bha seo? Nach faigheamaid uair sam bith cead a dhol a-null?

Air còrsachan mòr-thìre, a' coimhead a-null a Chanada às an Roinn Eòrpa, sheas mi air laimrig Telford ri faire a-null

57

dhan eaglais bhig a thog e fhèin le trannsa beag na dhìon an aghaidh sìde nan seachd sian. Cridhe mòr aig an duine, a' cuimhneachadh air na daoine fiù 's am-measg innleachd slighe ùr a' Ghlinne. An cothrom, mu dheireadh thall, faighinn tarsainn na Linne Duibhe, fiòrd na h-Alba, an Cuan Siar fhèin. An sgoltadh mòr, bho Shualbard Nirrbheach, a' gearradh na Gàidhealtachd na dà leth, agus às an sin, a-mach dhan chuan àrd.

Ghabh mi orm.

Chaidh mi air bòrd a' bhàt-aiseig, a bheireadh à Loch Abar Iarach mi don duthaich ùir, tarsainn caolais chumhaing, le sruth is làn a' sìor-strì an aghaidh a' chèile. A' togail rubhachan gnìobach de dh'uisge air taobh-sàil na laimrige; cumhachd gaoithe is a' ghealaich a' diùltadh gèilleidh.

Caolas a ghiùlainn dròbhairean, reubairean, croitearan, uachdairean, sgoilearan, ceòladairean. Fir is mnathan, clann, muinntir a' chinne-daonna. Aiseag ghoirid le eachdraidh fhada. Sgiobair a' crochadh bho ràmhan fhèin, mar leasan ann an dìlseachd bhon teaghlach aig a bheil fhathast, air èiginn, greim air an fhearann. Loch Iall 's Àird Ghobhar a' ceannach fearainn bho chèile, gus cas air gach taobh fa leth a bhith aig an dithis. Ceòl, ceòl air gach taobh, aig Mac an Tòisich is Mac Rath is eile, sna taighean-seinnse, beò le muinntir an àite. Aon thaigh air fhàgail a-nise. "A' tae wan side, like Gourock".

Chaidh mi a-null.

Cha b' ann gur rithist a thuig mi na trì mionaidean sin a bhi nan triall-farraige, bho sheann chreagan Eòrpach gu fìor chreagan àrsaidh Ameirigea. An dà thìr mhòir air am brùthadh ri guaillibh a-chèile, gus gleann a dhèanamh de chuan. Air a

bhith air taobh thall a' chaolais, taobh na Morbhairne, taobh
Àrd nam Murchan. Bha mi, a-nis, air an tìr eile. Na h-eilth-
irich a chaidh às an seo, a-null thar chuain; bha iad fhathast
air an aon thalamh. Chan ioghnadh gun do mhair an ceangal.

Bheachdaich mi.

Bha mi 'an dràst' an àit' ùr'. Àite far am faodadh ual-
lach fhàgail as mo dhèidh, gadaraich na beatha làitheil',
cunntasan, argamaidean, laigsean, mì-chinnt.

An uair a thuig mi an t-astar, a bha mi air siubhal, rinn e
ciall. Carson nach biodh cead ann, a-nise, dèanamh air àras
na h-oighreachd, far an robh àiteach is cruthachadh de sheòrsa
eile, a-nise, a' dol. Fuinn, ceòl, guthan, no gàire? Bha mi air
tighinn dhachaigh - nan robh fios agam air an uairsin. Bha mi
air siubhal thall thairis – trì mionaidean, leth-mhìle – is air
ruigheachd cladaichean ceanalta.

Thuig mi.

Aig a' chaolas seo, bha air 'ais 's air adhart' de sheòrsa eile a'
dol. Clò ùr ga fhighe: aodach lùbte gach pasgadh creige; reib-
hleas nam beanntan len snuadh sneachda. Sròl dubh-dhorcha
na Linne, le doimhneachd a' ruigheachd cho fada sìos 's a bha
na stùcan ag èirigh.

Ach 's iad sin snàth-cuir an spàil.

'S iad clann nan daoine an snàth dlùtha. 'S ann acasan, mar
ghiuthais Albannach nan gleanntan beaga air a' chladach
a-tuath, acasan a tha na freumhan a' gròbadh sìos, sìos dhan
ùir, dhan chreig, dhan domhan fhèin. Sliochd nan iomadh
ginealach, no meanglan ùr air a phòsadh ri stoc-freumhach nan
linntean. 'S ann acasan a tha na sùilean, a' coimhead a-mach

59

bhuapa, thar nead an dòbhrain, raon-cluiche na peileige, àit-eòlais na ròin. Às an sin gu h-àrd, ag amharc gach eun air ite; corra-ghritheach, lach fiadhaich, clamhan, iolaire. A' leigeil le macmeanmna dèanamh air sgèith, suas dha na speuran, gu iarmailt fhosgailte saorsa, dòchais, is na dh'fhaodadh a bhith. Bho na creagan shìos gu na speuran shuas; à cridhe na cruinne, gu taobh thall tuigse.

Bha mi aig ceann-uidhe. Chuir mi umam an t-aodach seo.

Thòisich mi air òran ùr.

An Gearastan gu Glaschu – Am Màrt 2016

Caolas (Narrows)

A Meditation on the Corran Narrows, Travelling in Hope, and the Possbility of the Far Side. Or this One

By Màiri Anna NicUalraig (Mary Ann Kennedy)

Highly commended in prose: 2015-16

(Originally written in Gaelic and translated by the author)

I stood there.

I stood on the banks of the loch, looking over to an unknown country, unfamiliar except in passing. Passing, each year, each time we would be headed for the Island, having crossed over Loch Leven with the cars birling the ferry waltz there, maintaining our northerly course. Me in the back, always wondering what this strange and exotic place might be, that we never had permission to cross over?

On the shores of a continent, looking over from Europe to Canada. I stood on Telford's slipway, looking over to the little church he built, with its bespoke porch a shelter from the elements: a compassionate man who remembered ordinary folk even amongst the lofty demands of a new route through the

Glen. A chance at last to cross over Loch Linnhe - the Black Water, Scottish fjord, the Atlantic itself. The great slash from Svalbard, slicing the Highlands in two, and from there out into the high seas.

I carried on.

I boarded the ferry that would bear me from Nether Lochaber to this new country – across a narrow stretch where tide and current battled restlessly, raising great headlands of water on the salt-side of the slipway, the power of wind and moon refusing to yield.

A crossing bearing drovers, reivers, crofters, landowners, scholars, singers – men and women, children, all humanity. A short crossing with a long story. A ferryman hung from his own oars as a lesson in loyalty from the family who still now, though barely, retain their hold on the land. Locheil and MacLean exchanging parcels of land to allow each a foothold astride the loch. Music, music on either side, from Mackintoshes, MacRaes and the rest, and the change-houses alive with locals. Just the one hostelry left now. 'A' tae wan side, like Gourock.'

I crossed over.

It was only later that I understood the three-minute journey for the sea-pilgrimage it truly was, from the old rocks of Europe to the ancient ones of America. The two continents pressed shoulder-to-shoulder, making a glen of an ocean. Standing now on the other side of the narrows, the Morvern - the Ardnamurchan side, I was now in another land. The emigrants from here, who headed overseas? They were still standing on familiar ground – small wonder the connection did not fail.

I contemplated.

I was 'now in a new place', to quote the song. A place where one might leave behind worry, the detritus of daily life, bills, arguments, frailties, insecurity.

When I understood the distance I had travelled, it made sense. Why not now make for the Home Farm, home now to another kind of husbandry and creation: melody, music, voices, laughter? I had come home, did I but know it then. I had journeyed abroad – three minutes, a half-mile – and reached home.

I understood.

At these narrows, there was a criss-crossing of a different kind going on – a new cloth being woven: folded layers of rock-cloth, mountain ruffles, lacy with snow, the impenetrable silken darkness of the loch reaching as far down as the peaks rose upwards.

But they are the product of the shuttle.

Humankind the warp-threads. Theirs – like the Scots pine that grow in the north shore's little glens – theirs are the roots that work their way down, down into the earth, the rock, creation itself, the descendants of infinite generations or new graft on centuries' rootstock. Theirs the eyes gazing out over otter's holt, porpoise's playground, familiar territory of seal; and from there upwards, observing each bird on the wing – heron, wild duck, buzzard, eagle, up into the skies to the wide-open heavens of freedom, hope and what might be. From the rocks below to the skies above – from the heart of the world to the far side of understanding.

I was at my destination. I put on this clothing.

And I began a new song.

Fort William to Glasgow – March 2016

Rambles of a Geologist

By Bob Davidson

Chairman of The Friends of Hugh Miller

After one of my early visits to Hugh Miller's Cromarty and his Birthplace Cottage nearly thirty years ago, I was keen to acquire a copy of *The Old Red Sandstone*. Calling by an Inverness bookseller on the way home, I found what I was looking for, an umpteenth edition for the sum of £30. Over the years this has been joined by my working copy - a seventh edition - and, taking pride of place on my bookshelf, a first edition. On my first deliberations of the contents, I was drawn in by the eloquence of the writing, the descriptive nature of the language and the insights that Miller was able to convey to the reader. This was, after all, at a time when authors practised the craft of raising script to the level of powerful poetry to convey their story to an increasingly demanding readership.

The 1800s was a time of public clamour for information, when both the heyday of natural history and the industrial revolution would overlap as a backdrop to an increasingly sophisticated Victorian society. Having been exposed to elements of industrialisation as a quarryman, and then in commerce, Hugh's vantage point as editor of *The Witness* provided him with a broad church upon which his writings would draw. In this article, I will present some of my favourite descriptive gems from his scientific writings.

Ichthyodorulites

In *The Old Red Sandstone*, Miller was pioneering popular science with an informed technical slant as he strove to recount the geology of Scotland, comparing it to that of England, making valiant attempts to name and correlate the subdivision of sedimentary rocks. Here, Miller demonstrates that he was talented in the use of devices to inform the reading classes through sculptural and, to an extent, romantic writing and the adept use of Greco Latinisms. One such example is pages 159-160 of the seventh edition where he figures fragments of fossil spines from an extinct fish from the Midland Valley of Scotland. The figure is captioned 'Balruddery spines' after the locality where they were found, but throughout the text he chose to describe them, somewhat flamboyantly, as 'ichthyodorulites'. One could be forgiven for speculating that Miller coined such a tongue twister to bestow importance on such unassuming objects. The fact is that the term was already in use and, subsequently, in his 1865 *Handbook of Geological Terms*, David Page gives the etymology of ichthyodorulite;

> *Greek. ichthys, fish; doru, spear; lithos, stone. A stone fish spear.*

In selecting it over a bland English descriptive term, Miller elevates the specimens' context in a way that only classical language can.

The Eigg Massacre

Nowhere does Miller better articulate an historical observation in direct contrast to his modern world than in chapter two of *The Cruise of the Betsey*. On visiting the infamous Cave of Frances (Uamh Fhraing) on Eigg, where clan rivalry between the MacLeods and the MacDonalds descended to the mass murder of all the MacDonald population of the island, Miller came upon a horse tooth among the bones of a child victim on the cave floor. Concluding that no horse could have fitted through the narrow entrance he speculated that it was carried in, perhaps as a child's toy, some final comfort in the face of the horrific events to come. Miller describes finding a tooth-bearing human jaw in this charnel house cave and remarks at its harmless appearance.

He goes on to compare his erstwhile discoveries of the fossil teeth of giant fish and reptiles as 'cruel spikes' and 'dagger like' and that there can be no mistaking the nature of the creatures to which they belonged. These were teeth designed for hacking, tearing and mangling. Man, by contrast, while capable of destroying creatures of his own kind, and in their hundreds, exhibits no such evidence of his true character in his dentition. He sums up all of this in the simple but lucid statement; 'Man must surely have become an immensely worse animal than his teeth show him to have been designed for.'

Miller knew what he was talking about, world events demonstrate that this remains the case to this day.

The *Cephalaspis* and the Saddler's Knife

Returning to *The Old Red Sandstone*, and to the Midland Valley, Miller describes the source of his ichthyodorulites during a visit to Balruddery Den, and the curious fossil fishes that were now emerging as the result of quarrying for farm walls and building stone. Miller's exuberant and convoluted attempt to fully describe the fish's strangeness to the reader is one of the greatest joys in this classic work.

> In the last mentioned locality, in a beautiful wooded dell known as the Den of Balruddery, the *Cephalaspis* is found associated with an entire group of other fossils, the recent discovery of Mr Webster, the proprietor who, with a zeal through which geological knowledge promises to be materially extended, and at an expense of much labour, has made a collection of all the organisms of the Den yet discovered. The *Cephalaspis* is one of the more curious ichthyolites of the system. Has the reader ever seen a saddler's cutting knife; - a tool with a crescent shaped blade, and the handle fixed transversely in the centre of its concave side? In general outline the *Cephalaspis* resembled this tool, the crescent shaped blade representing the head, the transverse handle the body. We have to give the handle an angular instead of a rounded shape, and to press together the pointed horns of the crescent till they incline towards each other, and the convex or sharpened edge is elongated into a semi elipse cut in the line of its shortest diameter, in order to produce the complete form of the *Cephalaspis*.

He could have referred the reader to the excellent

engraving of a complete fish in plate ten, figure one of this seminal work and left it at that, but Miller is true to his perceived mantra: Why squander a sentence when several paragraphs of vibrant prose will do?

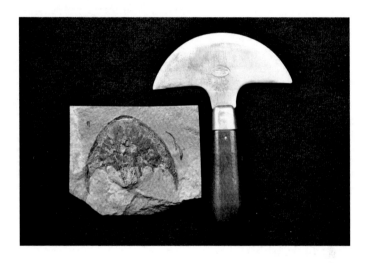

# of rocks in inundated darkness

BY ANNABELLE FULLER

UNDER-16 1ST PRIZE IN POETRY: 2015-16

each burnished flagstone sits steady,
unperturbed by shuffling scrapes.

yellow sandstone cliffs glare down,
abrupt and harsh, ruffians cloistered in imposing
grandeur,
casting gloom over the plucky flags.

no house can sleep beneath this twilight murk,
no chimney-breaths below the airless umbra.

morasses lie low,
deep, and black…
thick and viscous;
peaty lamentations.
sorrow bubbling.

above - precarious spots,
the hopeful grass that dares to grow,
take root in treacle misery.
red sandstone tries to raise its burning head.

looking on: the master stone,
unhewable,
unknowable,
a solid mass, colossus,
gatepost to the gods.

shrinking away, timid,
the baby caves of man.
dug up, two tiny squares,
plunging deep into the lonely earth.
mosses grow, cling to flinty sides,
stony pillow, boulder bed, divan of feather pebbles.

then thunder growls a warning, summoning clouds.
grey with misery, they collect as one, a seething mass of
expectation.
wind gales drop and rise,
crowding sequestered valley caverns.
air warm brooding heavy maternal.

blackness encumbers,
water dashing stones turned dark and cold.
buffeting the wild heather,
endlessly stampeding green grasses.

it batters down upon my lonely cell.
blanket sky-drenched,
stones whispering their secrets.

Una Mackenzie

BY MACKENZIE ERIN ROBBIE

UNDER-16 1ST PRIZE IN PROSE: 2015-16

The sun is falling in the sapphire blue sky, I'm going to collect water for máthair. As I walk, menacing black rocks are trying to burst out of the sea and land as if trying to reach the sunlight, if they were people they would not care about the chaos they are causing everywhere.

I pump water from the well into the pales, the icy cold water splashes up my arms. Huge rock cliffs surround me like a fence. As I walk I see the islands also have the pain of having rocks bursting through their land. There are no rolling hills on which you can run without a care in the world instead these hills have been taken by rocks and as you walk, you have to watch every step you take.

The sun is sinking behind the unforgiving mountains across the calm blue sea. Athair will be arriving home from working in the slate quarries. The walls and floors of the quarries are jagged and dangerous and as the men blow it up and chip away at the slate, it finally escapes from the darkness of underground, the iron pyrites glisten in the sun light as if celebrating.

Every Rolled Pebble
a Casket...

BY ELIZABETH PICKETT

HIGHLY COMMENDED IN POETRY: 2015-16

Desert lakes stacked high
tell Orcadian sagas
on flags of red-gold.

Slow Archaean birl
of pyroxene and feldspar
captured in Assynt.

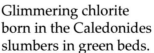

Glimmering chlorite
born in the Caledonides
slumbers in green beds.

Rippled sea-grey silk
hewn from Atlantic islands
skims the still water.

Silver graptolites
write of lost Iapetus
in a crumbling cleuch.

Broken magma road
stretches darkly back to Mull
stitching the Border.

Crawling Cards from Time Out of Mind

By Jim Gilchrist

3RD PRIZE IN PROSE: 2015-16

And then there rose in quick succession
scenes of the old Carboniferous forests: long
withdrawing lakes, fringed with dense thick-
ets of the green Calamite, tall and straight as
the masts of pinnaces, and inhabited by enormous fishes, that glittered through the trans-
parent depths in their enamelled armour
of proof; or glades of thickest verdure,
where the tree-fern mingled its branch-like
fronds with the hirsute arms of the gigantic
club-moss...

Hugh Miller, *Sketch-book of Popular Geology*, 1869.

Who can wait quietly while the mud settles?
Lao Tzu, *Tao Te Ching*, 4th Cent. BCE.

Both quotations come to mind while I'm standing on
the rocky shore near Crail harbour, contemplating
winter sunshine glimmer off two fossilised *Lepidodendron*
stumps, the gigantic club-moss of the Carboniferous forests evoked in that pre-cinematic, diorama-like sweep of
prose so characteristic of Hugh Miller.

I've known these hefty stumps since childhood holidays in the East Neuk of Fife. Much more recent was the realisation that, just a few yards away, the exposed sedimentary bedding is pitted by the tracks of a giant, centipede-like arthropod, all six feet of it, that was rattling about under these trees when the Scottish Lowlands were a complex of swampy lagoons and steaming forests, the remains of which would eventually form our coal seams.

Miller imagined something of the same: 'A huge crustacean of uncouth proportion stalks over the weedy bottom, or burrows in the hollows of the bank ...' There again he could almost have been referring to another Fife beastie of that period, *Hibbertopterus*, a two-metre long sea scorpion related to present-day arthropods such as scorpions and horseshoe crabs. Its trackway, found a few years ago in north-east Fife, revealed the crescent-shaped footprints and central tail groove it left while crossing wet sand 330 million years ago.

The trackway of a giant sea-scorpion, or Eurypterid, in sandstone at St Andrews, Kinkell Braes, Fife.

Also at Crail, as elsewhere around the East Neuk, you find perfectly preserved tidal ripples from those

Carboniferous mud flats, just as Miller, as an apprentice stonemason, found himself unearthing when blasting quarry rocks. 'The entire surface was ridged and furrowed like a bank of sand that had been left by the tide an hour before,' he recalled in *The Old Red Sandstone*.

Such frozen moments ... A friend of mine, the sculptor Tim Chalk, was commissioned to create a sundial around a fossil tree stump much like those at Crail for the garden in Edinburgh's Rutland Square. The elegant result sets the fossil stump against a contemplative bench bearing a spherical equatorial sundial fashioned like a split boulder. The fossil is encircled by sculpted glass-reinforced concrete, inscribed with fallen leaves and that quote from the *Tao* of Lao Tzu: 'Who can wait quietly while the mud settles?'

If time, according to Tennyson (a reader of Miller's *The Old Red Sandstone*), is a maniac scattering dust, he scatters no end of ancient footprints too. A few years ago, I had the chance to visit some fossil tracksites in Wyoming while driving north through the cowboy state with my wife, headed for Yellowstone. Surrounded by the spectacularly riven scenery of the Bighorn Basin, we jolted gingerly down a dirt road, trying not to lose our hired car's exhaust system and avoiding a basking rattlesnake, to emerge at Red Gulch Dinosaur Tracksite. There, amid a classic 'badlands' landscape, a gully floor is criss-crossed with smallish three-toed dinosaur prints, including those thought to be of the small raptor *Coelophysis*, similar to the types which also seem to have stalked the Isle of Skye, back in the Middle Jurassic period, when Scotland and North America were part of a common landmass*. The prints are preserved along

---

* Editor's note: a small seaway separated Scotland and North America at this time.

with the solidified ripples and worm holes of an ancient lagoon, again as if the tide had only just newly ebbed away, rather than 167 million years ago.

In this oil and mineral-rich state, geology is a pre-eminent concern and for many years the state's pre-eminent geologist was the celebrated David Love, who died in 2002. Working with the United States Geological Survey for more than four decades, Love, as writer John McPhee puts it in his fine book *Rising from the Plains*, was a man with 'the geologic map of Wyoming in his head'. He was, moreover, the son of a ruggedly individualistic Wyoming rancher, John Love, who had been born in Portage, Wisconsin, but educated in Scotland, the nephew of none other than the pioneer environmentalist John Muir. Muir was also someone who had a great regard for Hugh Miller's works, to the extent that he named an Alaskan glacier after him. And as Millar's books were, according to his protégé Archibald Geikie, 'to be found in the remotest log hut of the Far West', it seems as likely as not that they were also present in the remote Wyoming ranch house where Love junior grew up.

Owing to the fossil-rich nature of rock formations bearing such memorable names as Chugwater, Bighorn and Sundance (and, yes, Butch and the Kid roamed here), dinosaurs are something of a cottage industry in Wyoming, and the Wyoming Dinosaur Museum at Thermopolis is a dinophile's delight, although the fossil that stuck most in my mind was of a more modest if oddly affecting nature. It was of a small horseshoe crab, *Mesolimilus walchi*, a distant and diminutive Jurassic relative of that giant water scorpion that once prowled Fife. Unearthed in Bavaria, it was unusual in that it preserved not only the little armoured creature itself but also its tracks, recording clearly how some 150 million years ago it had progressed erratically along the muddy bottom for several metres, becoming increasingly disoriented, before grinding to a very terminal halt, for its body lay, perfectly etched, at the end of its final crawl. Horseshoe crabs survive as 'living fossils' to this day, and in Massachusetts I've seen beaches littered with their cast-off, helmet-like shells, like detritus from another age.

It has been suggested that possibly the creature found itself in toxic water, and tried fruitlessly to escape. Time and tide, as they say, wait for no man, but just some-times they do freeze-frame, to preserve for hundreds of millions of years a last, futile struggle for survival.

Romer's Gap

BY JUSTIN SALES

1ST PRIZE IN POETRY: 2015-16

Locked in lochans the cold winter long

Warped by forces of freeze and thaw

Silent amorphities of trapped air
Shivering beneath the ice
Assemble themselves
Bestir and quicken
Gain definition
Coalesce
Melt

Sep
arate

As the bubbles

burst!

Water
Flings
Itself
Down

                                          Hillsides
                              while
          gases   and
                         trace elements
                                        are flung
     to   the   four
                                            winds
             molecules fizzing
                              glittering and glinting
like microscopic strands of gossamer
                         caught between the peaks
                                        at dawn
             wheeling   over the
                        low   waves
                                    at dusk

             exulting in the entropy of it all
Air is free, water never
      From the first tentative
          Drip, drip, drip
            To the churning
                Of the tides
                    Water accumulates
      First pooling along the stems of the new grass
                         Then tripping
                In rivulets
                And down ravines
            Smashed apart
        By every rock
      Then brought together again
By gravity or God's will or merely fate
      To cycle round ever again
          For another go

From the infinite possibilities
Of bound and rebound
Comes one outcome
Only one
Only
Ever
One
This one

Beneath the bubble of the atmosphere
The rocks move, shift, settle and seethe
Fossils swim upwards again
Surfacing together in ancient shoals
Exposed by wind and wave and hammer

Evidence of life fixed in place aeons ago is uncovered
Creatures somewhere between fish and fowl
Teeth skittering across the rocks
Bones shadowy to non-existent
Hands with too many fingers
Grasp at the air of an unfriendly sky

There's a gap
Where fins become legs
When fish became lizards
(Or, at least, semi-terrestrial limbèd vertebrates)

Between the Devonian and the Carboniferous
After the armoured fishes
And before the coal-bequeathing trees

Not much oxygen then
Not many species
Not many fossils now

But they are emerging, slowly
Along the shores and the riverbanks
The shingles and the strands
Near Bass Rock and along the Whiteadder
Lungfish and other tetrapods
Crawling out of history
With questions

And here they come in turn
The fossil hunters
Keeping their own time
Backpacks and bubble-wrap
And a look in their single-lensed eyes
That speaks
Of weeks
Spent scrabbling on beaches like this one

Washing up along the shore each morning
Swept back at nightfall
To warm pubs and cold tents
Lingering over a sunset
Or returning later to see the moon
    A silver highway across the sea
Ponderous

    How big was the moon back then?
About the same size, less a few asteroids
    How big did it *appear*?
About the same size, allowing for a slightly smaller
orbit
    But I saw this programme where the sky was a
different colour...
Because of the methane?
    What?
Never mind

Busy busy busy
Trying to understand everything
While there's still time

Another gap looms

Meanwhile information continues to accrue
Multiply
Inform
Transform
Take on a life of its own

Words scribbled in a notebook
Twenty years ago on Skye
Are unearthed to appear
Blinking
On the screen
Adapting and evolving
Adopting new configurations
And diverging

To live
Thrive
And survive

Trying to fit new conditions

Lines upon lines
Strata
Errata
Encoded data
Revealing just enough
To have a chance
Of living forever

Fossils of the Mind

By Elsa Panciroli

> The only fossils described in my present chapter are fossils of the mind.
>
> Hugh Miller, *The Cruise of the Betsey*, 1858.

I am the last to leave the Island of Mists. The rest of the team has already folded their hike-sore limbs into their cars for the long journey south - Highlands, Lowlands, England. I watch them slide tentatively over the single-track road as I close the sheep-gate. When the car engine has rumbled over the brow of the Strathaird Peninsula, I am left standing alone on the threshold of our rented cottage, kissed by the sunshine of Skye.

I could lie down right here and sink into the Hebridean peats. A bog-woman. A Scottish Oetzi. Wake me up next year, then we'll go fossil-hunting together again.

But instead I walk inside and leave the key on the table. At the window I drink in one last dram of the Cuillin. Climbing into the van, I set off for Kyleakin and the bridge to the mainland.

* * *

The small boat was dragged easily from the harbour and out into the sound. The rough hand of the wind pushed it towards Eilean Bàn. Miller watched the handsome houses of Kyleakin drifting away from him. Above them, the ruins of Castle Maol: torn in two as if by an earthquake. He turned away from Skye and toward his destination: the open mouth of Loch Carron.

As the boat passed the blackened skerries, skittish seals caterpillared into the waters of the Sound. They watched from the safety of the thick kelp beds, their eyes big and wet. Soon the small vessel had passed the land jutting out north of Kyle of Lochalsh, and sailed into the shelter of the sea-loch. Miller eyed the dark brooding clouds lining the horizon above Strathcarron.

By the time they reached the harbour at North Strome, the rain had begun. Miller pulled his woollen maud tighter. He disembarked. The first drops of rain sprinkled themselves on his shoulders as he set off along the jetty in search of transport east.

* * *

The road intensely roller-coasters up through the forests from Loch Alsh, only to relax down into the U-shaped valley of Strathcarron. I meet the T-junction heading eastwards, and lower my boot to pick up speed. The van whizzes along the blue tongue of road that licks its way west to east across the Highlands.

Behind me, Loch Carron and the West Coast are soon lost. At first I wind through trees laced with Victorian introductions like rhododendron and redwood. I turn a corner and come face to face with an explosion of early-spring blooms, blushing in front of a sandstone mansion. A wealthy estate: they used to lodge monarchs, now they entertain oligarchs. Further on, the planted woodlands give way to a deep gorge, with Scots pine forest sitting on its shoulders.

As the road ascends, the woodland thins and the miles between Loch Carron and Dingwall are sparse and windswept. A short shaggy coat of russet grass and heather covers the hills, and you feel as though you are a flea traversing the back of a Highland cow. Water collects in the wide valleys, forming glinting lochans. The mountains are worn like cue-tips, and water has scoured rivulets down their faces, carrying pink and grey rocks along the gushing streams.

I think of the ice that squatted over these high lands and rubbed itself up against the barren stones. Sometimes it carried a rock down from the hilltops in its frozen pockets. Turning it over and over through the deepening glens to be deposited elsewhere. Millennia later, humans would puzzle over these erratic collections, and find in them evidence of an age of ice that covered Scotland.

In the back of my vehicle, plastic boxes scrape along the floor as I turn a corner. My team have rock collections of their own. I'm carrying them in my white van, downhill, downstream, to their new destination in the low lands. They will be puzzled over by a new generation of scientists: they have stories to tell us.

* * *

The rain pelted into the passengers on the carriage, making them shiver. In the front seat Miller sat beside the mail-gig driver. The driver barely had to guide his horses - they clearly knew the track, and trotted onwards into the wind with their heads down, pulling their heavy load.

In the back the other passengers chatted to pass the time, but their voices didn't carry easily to Miller. He tried to engage the driver in conversation, but although he nodded amiably, he didn't offer any words of his own. The pair fell into companionable silence.

The mail-gig stopped at Janetown, where a man approached and asked for passage to Dingwall. A minister from the local Church of Scotland. The driver nodded and waved him on, but pulling himself stiffly up into the carriage, he saw there were no seats left.

"Where am I to sit?" he asked. The taciturn driver indicated a narrow platform between the front and back of the gig, just wide enough for a man to squeeze into. The minister looked at the other passengers hopefully. They stared blankly back at him. With a resigned grumble he folded himself into the cramped space. Miller smiled: in his dark clothes and with the grey whisps of whiskers on either side of his face, the minister looked like a hedgehog settling in his nest to hibernate.

The gig set off again, picking up pace as it left the shore and entered the wide valley of the River Carron. The weather relaxed into a grey drizzle as they moved along the valley bottom. The clouds hung low, as though held up by the surrounding hilltops like a tent canvas. The horses shook their heads to loosen the water from their dripping manes. Behind Miller and the diver, the minister muttered to himself moodily. Miller couldn't tell if his words were of complaint or prayer - they were often one and the same anyway.

Not far beyond the parish they passed a collection of little bumps in the terrain. The land undulated, and each rise was tufted with dark brown heathers, like a bonnet. Miller turned to the Minister, who was still mumbling in his nest.

"What fine moraines, formed from a long-gone glacier" he said to him, tilting his head towards the gravel hummocks. "How much more dreary the prospect must have been when these bleak-hillsides and hollows were blocked up with ice."

The Minister startled at the unexpected attention. He straightened up enough to look at the moraines. He regarded Miller quizzically, noting his plaid trousers and the black and white wool blanket wrapped around him. His face still stern, he agreed, "Indeed, a great deal more disagreeable."

Miller noted the deep wrinkles on the man's face, seeing how he winced as he lowered himself back into his cramped position. He was clearly much older than his crisp ministerial airs let on, at least sixty or seventy years.

Miller shifted in his seat in the front, perching himself at the furthest edge from the driver. A gap opened up between them. He indicated to the driver to do the same, who wordlessly obliged, creating a space just large enough for a third man to squeeze between them.

"Look," he said, turning to the Minister again, "There is space enough for you to join us here. Won't you sit?"

The old man's eyes widened with delight, and with Miller's help he clambered unsteadily over the back of the bench and sat down. Out of his burrow, he was transformed: his eyes glittered in the fog, and he smiled warmly.

As the mail-gig moved upland, the minister told Miller about the quality of the pasture in the farms they passed: "The flocks here thrive steadily, and are not thinned by disease," he said. Pointing back downriver he added, "Although the herbage is richer along the valley bottom, at the close of autumn the braxy falls upon the flocks like a pestilence. The superior fertility of the soil is no advantage in such a case."

The minister seemed particularly interested in the conditions of the surrounding farmland, talking in great detail about the benefits and drawbacks of each pasture-land, and the owners and their attitude. Miller was surprised – until realising he had mistaken him for a shepherd. In his plain trousers and shepherd's check cloak, the minister must have thought Miller had travelled north from the borders looking for work on a Highland farm. Would he be so friendly if he knew the truth about his new companion?

Miller listened politely – it wasn't uninteresting, but soon he steered the talk to other subjects. The pair chatted easily as beneath them the carriage wheels rolled on through the drizzle towards Dingwall.

* * *

Beyond Achnasheen, the van carries me on the last stretch before Garve. On my right I follow the meander of the cold River Bran upstream to the small Lochs of Achanalt and a'Chuillin. On the left, Forestry commission firs huddle together in dark bands on the hillside. A train appears and races me eastwards. There are only two carriages, and I consider stopping at the small station at Achanalt to see who might board and alight here in this windswept valley. I am envious.

This stretch was notorious for accidents when I was a girl. West Coasters returning with cars full of shopping from Inverness regularly smashed into startled red deer, which moved between the upland and the valley bottom as night fell. There was always a freshly crumpled car on the roadside when you passed through.

A small building beside the road catches my eye. I slow the van to take another look - my thousandth-or-so since childhood. A cottage is perched about ten metres from the verge. It is made of neat pink and grey stones, a perfectly symmetrical single-story with two front windows and a vestibule, all topped in slate. A typical Victorian build. It has barely changed in the last thirty years – probably the last one-hundred-and-thirty. A bit more dilapidated perhaps, with a few extra holes in the roof, and the windows now boarded up by a conscientious estate owner.

"There's a doer upper for you!" I say aloud to myself in the van, seeing as my parents aren't there to say it to me, as they always do. This wild and derelict cottage, perfect for this wild and derelict daughter. A landmark on my family's many journeys east and west. It is half-way between. No matter where I end up living, part of me always lives here.

* * *

At last the carriage descended the final stretch towards the inn at Garve, leaving the bleak uplands behind in their cloak of rain. The inn sat above the black waters of the An t-Alltan Dubh, a river Miller knew was rich with pike, trout and salmon. The valley led downstream to Dingwall, and although the long and soggy journey east had passed quickly with their lively conversation, a long final leg lay ahead.

When the driver hopped off and began changing horses, Miller and the minister stood up stiffly, and tottered down from the gig. They had some time to wait, and decided to stroll along the track a little and continue their discussion. Miller noticed how the trees had been thinned by the eager axes of the locals, even since his last visit. As they passed a rocky outcrop where the soil had been washed away by heavy rain, he commented on the gneiss that was uncovered underneath, like flesh beneath a grazed knee.

Suddenly the minister turned to him, "We are not on equal terms," he said seriously. "You know who I am, and I don't know you." He looked into Miller's eyes as though searching for an answer to some conundrum.

Miller laughed and scratched his cheek beneath his reddish beard, "It is true, we have agreed hitherto, but I'm not sure how we are to agree when you know who I am…"

The minister looked wary, "We did not start fair at the beginning, but let us start fair now."

"Are you sure you will not be frightened?" Miller asked.

"Frightened!" The minister's voice hardened, "No. I am frightened by no man."

"Well then: I am the editor of *The Witness*."

The minister looked momentarily scandalised. He had spent the day in happy discussion with the man whose newspaper spoke vocally against the established Church. Scottish religious life had been forever divided by the evangelicals breaking away and forming their own ministry, the so-called Free Church. Here stood the household name who was a voice for the disruption: the writer, geologist, and stonemason Highlander.

After a long silence, the minister put out his hand and took Miller's. "Well," he said, somewhat breathlessly, "Give me, man, a shake of your hand."

Miller shook it gladly. The skin was delicate and thin, like bible pages.

"It's all the same. I'm glad we should have met."

The pair soon resumed their conversation. Back on the mail-gig with fresh horses, they travelled on through the wooded valley to Dingwall, each soaked to the skin and, despite their differences, happier to have shared the ride than to have made it alone.

* * *

As I come over the brow of the hill, I get the first glimpse of the east coast. The River Conan slips into the bay at Dingwall, sending its fresh waters out to mingle with the Cromarty Firth. I slow the van for the first time in miles, negotiating the roundabout that pivots me south.

After a few miles a second roundabout guards the entrance to the Black Isle. Third exit for Inverness. Beyond the Highland capital I have a few more hours to travel before reaching Edinburgh. One end of my heart is always looped around North-west Scotland, like an elastic band. It stretches thin and taught as I move further South. Only when I come back does it relax again.

The sign for Cromarty appears - for a moment I consider escaping. I could continue east until the road runs out in that handsome fishing port. I could wander along the shore turning rocks over until it gets dark.

The fossils in the back of the van rasp as I drive in an arc, around the roundabout again, missing all the turn-offs.

I think of Miller, heading back to Cromarty after his voyages through the Western Isles. He lingered for several days around the Black Isle, walking for miles over the paths of his memories, revisiting old haunts and picking up stones. But he, too, had to go South in the end. I wonder if he also felt torn in half every time? His soul forever catching fossil fish along the shoreline, but his head and his pen at the editorial desk in Edinburgh.

Like a leaf circling a whirlpool, I swirl around

again. The fossils gasp. I click down the indicator, and the van carries me South.

Miller's journey and his conversation with the minister were re-created based on his account of returning from the Isle of Skye in The Cruise of the Betsey *(1858, pages 159-161).*

Pneumodesmus newmani

By Alex Woodcock

1ST PRIZE IN POETRY: 2017-18

I was twenty-three,
Eight years before the discovery,
Breaking my back in the ceilidh
In Stonehaven

Drunk and wearing a kilt. The wedding lasted four
days,
The journey from York, six hours;
We arrived in the dark
And woke to the waves

But you were already there,
A scratch in the sandstone,
A feather on the finger of time
Hiding out in the cliffs

Waiting for the hammer.

We ate blueberries on the train up, I remember,
Something exotic, or so it seemed then,
Like the first air that you sipped
When Scotland was near the equator,

You, a whisper of life
Held by the rocks for
Over four hundred million years:
Pneumodesmus newmani.

The story goes
It was a local bus driver that broke you free,
A fossil collector when not at the wheel
And now the father of an ancient millipede,

Perhaps the first oxygen-breathing animal to live on land.
There's a photograph online,
A wide-toothed comb of stone
Transient as a scar

And no longer than a fingernail,
Legs floating like the tentacles of a jellyfish,
A beautiful arrangement by the sediments
Clearly thinking ahead.

We slipped in our smooth-soled shoes on the path
To Dunnottar Castle
And lined up in the rain and the ruins
As Tim and Claudia were married;

I have a picture somewhere,
A concentration of formal dress and umbrellas,
Of men with long hair and cold knees
And relatives sheltering beside masonry,

A moment in time
Of many moments in time,
As you waited

And waited for the one

When we had evolved
And had enough fortune on our side,
To find your tiny footprint
And recognise your pioneering life.

***

Now, in another life of my own,
Hundreds of miles south,
And walking the shore like Kenneth White
Ruminating on the rosy quartz,

Thinking of Okuizumi writing
'Even the smallest pebble in a riverbed
has the entire history of the universe
inscribed upon it',

Recalling Miller, a stonemason like myself,
Asleep and dreaming of the day's drab burial ground
'suffused with the blush of sunset',
the stones on which he'd only just worked

Antique and thick with moss and lichens;

Looking for echinoids below the chalk cliffs,
Sometimes finding one in the shingle
Like the other month,
Turning over a grey pebble

And realising it was a heart-shaped urchin, *Micraster*,

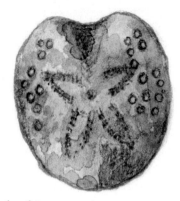

A mere slip of a thing
At around
Sixty million,

I'm thinking of that long weekend
(Still by far the best wedding)
And of all the undiscovered and unknown
Creatures beneath,

Their lives a faint cast or impression
Deep underground,
And of your emergence into our world
In the early two-thousands.

Well

All the Palaeozoic fishes,
All the smiths forging tools in the Iron Age,
All the bus drivers,
All the plants that have weathered

A life on the land,

All the artists and scientists,
All the animals silent in the glow of the moon,
All the feathered dinosaurs
Eating from the bird-table,

Salute you.

Landward

By Thomas Halliday

1st prize in prose: 2017-18

The sun reluctantly sklents beneath the clouds to cast long afternoon shadows along the strandline at Yellowcraig. A stiletto of an east wind blows in from the Bass, scattering the sand. I turn my back to the blast, away from the dog walkers and families, and down the narrow path between the buckthorn, the bents and the strand. The basalt isle of Fidra with its lighthouse sulks in the mist as I skirt the black rocks. Over my shoulder are towering volcanic plugs and the remains of bulging underground lakes of magma, silent reminders of a turbulent geological past. Berwick Law. The Lamb. Craigleith. The Bass. They disappear as I round the corner, this next bay sheltered by a stand of pines. It is quiet save for the distant thwack of golf balls to the laughter of fieldfare, as I see the dark Forth laid out before me.

Against the yellow sands, the shales and cement-stones are exposed. I crouch down to peer at the revealed rock pools. Crabs and brown shrimp flee from view, while thrawn limpets hold fast. A pebble of shale, recently detached and fractured, reveals the perfect white memory of a different shrimp, and a different coast.

Here, in this small bay, was once a freshwater lake

or lagoon, some three hundred and thirty million years ago – a time best known for its intense heat and congested mires of plant matter, congealing and transforming into peat and coal. The middle of the Viséan age, during which these rocks were laid down, was one of strong, monsoon-like seasons mixed with unpredictable periods of drought. The surface of the lake rose and fell, fed by tropical rains flowing through a vast, meandering river delta from northern hills now lost to time. The volcanoes that once overtopped the Law and Bass Rock were active and explosive, hot lava steaming in the mudflats. In those days the sun climbed higher in the sky, and the sheer heat of its direct, equatorial gaze was enough to separate the surface water from the drowning cold depths that, unable to muster enough energy to break the surface, became suffocated of oxygen. But for the rumbling of the earth from the young and petulant volcanoes, and the occasional intrusion of salt water from the nearby sea, the lake was calm and still – and was teeming with shrimp.

These fossil shrimp, beautiful though they are, are not why I am here. This is something of a pilgrimage, as one might make to the grave of a distinguished ancestor, even long after all who knew them are gone. For, among the crustaceans and plants, if one is lucky enough to find them, the hills and coastlines of southern Scotland hide ancient pioneers who lived alongside these ancient lakes. The oldest – and smallest – of them, *Casineria*, lived here at Yellowcraig. The fossil itself is unassuming; ribs, feet, and vertebrae scattered like a tangle of broom, headless, tailless, and small, but with a tale to tell.

With periodic droughts, the pools dotting the river delta would, from time to time, run dry. For the amphibious four-legged beasts that populated the freshwater pools and swamps, this was a problem. In the long heat of an extended drought, and without water to lie in, the soft, wet eggs would desiccate and die. One evolutionary innovation changed all that, and allowed a single small-bodied group of organisms to escape the confines of the water. A series of almost impossibly thin membranes within the egg: the allantois across which oxygen passes, and the protective chorion and amnion, providing a private pond allowing the embryo to grow, all surrounded by the armour of a shell. The eggs of the relatives of *Casineria* – my ancestors – would become strong enough to remove the need to reproduce in water. The whole of the terrestrial realm, from the lakeshores and riverbanks up to the highest mountain and into the driest desert, was suddenly habitable. That world had already been colonised twice, by plants and arthropods – insects, millipedes, arachnids – and was a landscape rich with food and opportunity. If I look around, there is nothing that is not as it is because of the tiny developmental shift from water-bound tetrapod to amniote.

The reach of *Casineria* and its kin has extended around and beyond the earth, shaping environments throughout that long 'yesterday of the globe' and into human history. All around this flattened landscape, settlements have sprung up around black-stained shafts driven down through time into the Carboniferous swamps, still influencing the global environment hundreds of millions of years later.

The name of this land, it is said, derives from Lot, the king of Arthurian legend who reigned atop another Carboniferous volcanic plug at Traprain Law. He, in turn, takes his name from Lleu, a legendary Brythonic demigod, who was said to be vulnerable to death neither during the day nor at night, neither clothed nor naked. He could not be killed indoors, or outside. Only when existing on the borderline, partially clad on a threshold at dusk, neither in one state nor another, was his mortality revealed. Here, in Lot's kingdom, between sea and shore, *Casineria* has cheated destruction. A single individual, whose life began within membranes within membranes and ended sinking into the unbreathing depths of an ancient lake. Compacted in layers of mud, avoiding volcanic fires, the easterly scraping of kilometre-thick ice, the tectonic yawns of the earth, and erosion by the tireless wind, *Casineria* has crossed a third of a billion years to show us the nature of its own liminal existence. A new kind of life, leaving the water behind. Neither amphibian, nor quite amniote, and yet a living whole.

The tired winter sun droops in the sky. The waves are returning, burying once more the ancient lake. The far-stretching stones thin and submerge. A single scoter distantly bobs in the current, still hopeful of shrimp. I turn, and climb the marram-knitted dune. My place is on the land.

After Life: Finding Tiny

By Fiona Ritchie Walker

Highly commended in poetry: 2017-18

Not so much rock as a stone womb,
preserving life lived, waiting for discovery,
pick and chisel replaced with discerning scan,
today's technology birthing
this 3D re-creation, which I have found
in a coffee break while flicking through headline news.

I'm drawn in by simple language,
Tiny's sharp teeth, dimpled chin,
that take me to the end of the age of fish,
my birth land straddling the equator,
and though I say I have no interest
in old Scottish rocks, Latin names,
I find Hugh Miller in my local library,
take his history home.

My tongue twists round Tournaisian,
I picture Tiny, her five digits pulling
our shared backbone, hinged jaw, lungs
through swamp water to lycopod forests,
towards today where my mirror fingers
hold a pen, record this life change

that has sent me to rocks and beaches,
museums and scree slopes,
tracking our shared journeying
in this world of air and land.

Echoes from Orcadie

By Kenny Taylor

Two summers ago, I saw a fish just recently washed up on a local beach. Not a fish with silvered scales, eyes clouding as they dried. A black fish, pressed flat on a grey stone shoved in by the waves of a recent storm. But this was no fish from any sea still swirling on earth. No creature of the here-and-now, with kindred shoaling offshore. Its eyes lost focus more than 370 million years ago, as it sank to the bed of a vast lake.

I would come to learn such details later. But here it was – a fossil fish, still glistening on a shore that had felt familiar, yet now, momentarily, was strange. As if the oil rigs across the bay and the dogs and their walkers nearby were not there; as if the calls of gulls and jackdaws over the houses once home to fisher folk and merchants and sea captains in Cromarty had fallen silent; as if all I could hear was the shush of surf, without sense of what sea, what time was pulsing it; as if the fish had once more swum, buoyed by the weeds on the stone but somehow freed from that matrix. And now I could hold it, wondering.

This was the biggest jolt yet; but for some years now, I've been stopped in mid-pace by traces of Orcadie, a series of lakes that grew and then shrank and vanished as continents collided and oceans closed. As the fortunes of ancestors rose and fell. More and more, I'm noticing rhythms of ancient flood and drought that show in stone. Or the ripples from a single tide, aeons old.

The deep past is pushing-in as I walk the coastlands of the Moray Firth and Orkney, along the margins of old Orcadie. And as it does so, my sense of the present is also changing, as I explore lines of thought in unfolding science, look for clues along sandy margins, find fresh ways of thinking about the writing of others who have studied and celebrated these shores and the rivers that run to them.

The exploration isn't linear, following a predictable sequence from place to place, from place to idea, though connections like that are sometimes possible. It's fragmentary, and for now, I can only describe some pieces. By gluing them together with words, I hope, perhaps naively, that they hint at wider patterns. Re-arrange them as you will.

***

Lake

Take sand and mud by the mountain load. Add to river water. Pour into a basin large enough to hold much of what is now Scotland. Keep pouring.

Let the rains fall, and fall. Few plants to stay the flow of torrents from the bare hills. Lake swells. Dunes are inundated, shorelines swamped. As deep as a hundred metres. As expansive as 50,000 square kilometres.

Turn up the heat. Water evaporates. Lake shrinks, now

more a dappling of deeper and shallower water-filled depressions than a single superlake.

The water heats. Oxygen dips. Primitive fish gasp. And as they expire, bodies bloated with decay float out to the middle of pools and sink down, down to muddy beds.

Dunes creep over what once was water, cover marks of wavelets, cracks in mud, bury corpses of fish. Rains return.

Take sand and mud by the mountain load. Add to river water. Pour.

Repeat.

Repeat.

Repeat over millions of years. Over tens of millions of years.

Compress. Make stone. Bury. Exhume. Crack.

Tilt.

***

Brodgar

Raise the flagstones; the flags; the monoliths. On a neck of land in the heart of the island, heave huge stones upright in a ring.

Stenness. The first. The place of the living. Now lay a causeway – the Ness - to link the first circle to a broader bulge of land. Build a wall across the procession way. Paint it red. Red as the western sunset, as the blood of sacrificed cattle.

Raise a second circle.

Brodgar. Ringed by ditch and dyke. Henge beyond the wall. The place of the dead.

Each stone an individual, each a fragment of lake bed and shore, morphed over millions of years from soft to hard, carrying marks and lines and traces of something ancient. Each shape unique.

Use the place for centuries, as people settle the fertile isles. Feast here, tell stories, raise dead to be picked clean by sea eagles and ravens and then place some of the bones in stone tombs nearby. Dance when the season-fires flame to life and shadows leap on the monoliths. See then that the stones dance with you.

Then leave the place. Leave it to the winds and rains and occasional summer heat of Orkney, to prise apart the layers and slough the stone skin, as people walk among them, not dancing.

***

Hugh Miller

He's walking the shore near his Cromarty home, this big man of broad brow and deep thatch of dark red hair. Mason's hammer in hand, he chips rocks by the sea at a place where a band of limestone meets the wider jumble of beach cobbles. Stones split, separating grey oval from grey oval.

Repeat.

Then a blow opens a large stone to reveal a dark stain. More than that – a shape; a fish-like shape, with scales and flattened head and fins so strange they look like tiny wings. Bird-like, almost.

Pterichyodes milleri.

Named for the wings. Named for the man.

Hugh Miller. Polymath. Stone mason. Self-taught geologist and later expert on fossils from Orcadie. Splitting rocks. Splitting religious factions. Splitting Free Church free from the weight of laird-imposed ministers.

Fossil fish. *Miller's Wing-Fish*. Wing-fish Miller. He lifts the stone and lets thoughts soar.

'Had Lamarck been the discoverer,' he wrote of that fossil find a decade later in *The Old Red Sandstone*, 'he would have unquestionably have held that he had caught a fish almost in the act of wishing itself into a bird.'

> …there are none of the fossils of the Old Red Sandstone which less resemble any thing that now exists than its *Pterichthys*. I fain wish I could communicate to the reader the feeling with which I contemplated my first found specimen. It opened with a single blow of the hammer; and there, on a ground of light-coloured limestone, lay the effigy of a creature fashioned apparently out of jet,

with a body covered with plates, two pow-
erful-looking arms articulated at the shoulders, a head as entirely lost in the trunk as
that of the ray or the sun-fish, and a long angular tail.

Old Red – both man and rock. Wing-fish Miller, noticing the smallest details of stones on the Cromarty shore,
then later at his desk, looking at the fossil before writing
the next line. Splitting time apart.

***

Stone wind

Ripples in the Old Red reveal patterns of flow and also
wind directions; the imprints of hot gales that once
threw desert sands skywards, the fall-out covering fish
bodies and shrinking the lake. Paleo-winds.

'In this study,' write the authors of a recent scientific paper, 'Middle Devonian paleo-wind directions are
reconstructed by measuring the orientation of 511 fos-
silized wave ripple marks in the Rousay Flagstone
Formation on the island of Westray, Orkney, Scotland,'
(De Vleeschouwer D., Leather & Claeys, 2015)

That statement both excites and inspires me; as if a
sudden gust of air from an unseen desert has blown on
the back of my neck. When I turn, it's gone. But I know
it was there.

Wind-blown or river-borne, lake deposits settle, form
bands of colour. Some are bright-coloured in reds and
yellows, others muddy grey. The thicknesses vary, but

there are patterns in how they lie. Rhythms.

Measure the layers; map the sequences; clock the pulses.

And in them, trace ripples that move from Orkney to beyond earth; to the way the planet slowly shifts its orbit in relation to our home star, and then back again. A cycle of one-hundred thousand years or so.

Repeat.

Look closer. There are other rhythms here: cycles that suggest sunspots, whose numbers rise and ebb every eleven years or thereabouts. Imprints from explosions whose particles surf space between sun and earth, riding waves of energy. The solar wind, held in stone.

***

Deep time

Rocks and the fossils within them helped Hugh Miller to sense something he could not see. To push away narrow readings of the bible, the mainstay of his religious belief, and eventually to yield, he said, to evidence he found impossible to resist. Sitting in Edinburgh, he works near-continuously, day and night, on *Testimony of the Rocks*, the book that would be his last. In it, he writes:

> 'That day during which the present creation
> came into being…was not a brief period of
> a few hours' duration, but extended over
> mayhap millenniums of centuries.
> … and so I have been compelled to hold,
> that the days of creation were not natural,

but prophetic days, and stretched far back
into bygone eternity.'

Hours after sending the final manuscript sheets of the
book to his publisher, Hugh Miller joins that bygone
eternity. But the ideas he communicated and the finds
he described remain; still discussed by those who relish
rocks for what they may hide and reveal; who appreciate the testimony they can give about past and present
and what might yet come to be.

His wing-fish still ride the tides where the Cromarty
shore touches Orcadie. So do others, just as ancient and
beautiful and strange. Like the one I saw two summers
ago, passed across to be held by a young girl as the wind
dried its scales.

She was smiling.

*A small part of the material in this piece was presented in
'Infinite Scotland', which toured Scottish theatres in 2013.
Some was also delivered as spoken-word performances at the
Scottish Centre for Geopoetics "Expressing the Earth" confer-
ence on the island of Luing in the summer of 2017 and at the
Highland Environment Forum in Inverness in the autumn of
that year.*

The First King of Scotland

By Gillian Dawson

Runner-up in poetry: 2017-18

Here he comes, jinking through the gloaming,
elated after a night vibrating
with chorusing frogs, chirruping crickets,
a teeming larder of insects' rasps and ticks.

He's learnt the skills of the hunt:
a rearing centipede disarmed with prowess,
the crunch of carapace between teeth,
his stomach taut from the feast.

Home-bound on the familial track
he scent-marks horsetails and tree-ferns
shimmering green on the lagoon
he drinks in the dawn, sits down to groom.

Milk teeth rooted in a stone jaw
exposed by the waves of a cold shore

Wareolestes rex: the first king of Scotland

Impressions

By Ross Barnett

Highly commended in prose: 2017-18

I was about six years old when I first tried to listen to the past. Holding a fossil ammonite to my ear I strained to catch a hint of prehistory, the way you can hear the seaside from a seashell. In a roundabout way, the experience coloured my whole life. I couldn't hear dinosaurs roaring or ichthyosaurs spouting through my little ammonite, but an early introduction to fossils and extinction boggled my growing mind so much that I've spent many of the years that followed immersed in remnants of ancient life. Little me was standing on the island of Raasay - a small, rarely visited scrap of land off the west coast of Scotland. Famous chiefly for entertaining Johnson and Boswell, having its own subspecies of bank vole, and its varied geology, Raasay is not on the tourist trail. The island was and is home to a fervently Presbyterian Free Church. My own dad (a lapsed geologist) took me fossil hunting here, and such is the abundance of material even a small child can find belemnites, ammonites, and the like. My mother's side of the family, in the beautiful Gaelic phraseology, belong to Raasay. In a way, I do too. My maternal connection ties me to the barest soil of this patchwork island. Linked to the family who entertained

Johnson, sheltered Prince Charlie. Memories of childhood summers tie me here with stronger bonds than just genetics.

I remember the first fossil trip, from the pre-Cambrian of my own life, with a startling vividity. We had set off from our wee caravan in Inverarish, the largest village on the island. Walking past the quiet houses. Walking past the silent playpark with the padlocked swings. There was rain, of course. You cannot visit the west coast in summer and avoid it. The drops bounced off the grass at the side of the path and mingled with the mud. The bracken, copious and verdant, was prehistoric in appearance, acting as a signpost to the past we were going to visit. Travelling east through fields of hardy sheep, I remember complaining, as small children do, about the distance, the weather, the time it was taking. Looking back now, I cannot ever remember being happier. Family united in a quest. A father wanting to share the joy of finding. A mother showing the places of her youth. A treasure hunt for understanding. I didn't realise any of this; I was six. When we got to the coast and I had been shown how to look for stones of the right size and shape I spent some time among the rocks getting my eye in and scrabbling around. Taking my finds to my father and dropping them at his feet he apported a small hammer and gently tapped each one. This was a new kind of magic. There were things inside. Stone cylinders that I learned were called belemnites: the cuttlebones of squidlike creatures that had swum in tropical seas. In one, there was part of a coiled shell: an ammonite. It reminded me of a seashell, I put it to my ear.

Since that summer, thirty years ago, so much has changed. I didn't know it at the time, but my mother was sick. She died a year later from the cancer that spiralled within her. I grew up and made the study of the past my career. A fractal hope that learning about fossils and extinction would help me to preserve knowledge of my own past. If only there was a taphonomy of the mind that could preserve memories and feelings the way the soft earth does! Since then I've striven to keep each memory of my early years properly curated. Each impression must be prepared correctly, adhering matrix removed, content inspected. In my private museum of the mind, I am the curator of memories. They can be taken off shelves for display. Replayed and rethought.

Sometimes they degrade. Sometimes, all I'm left is a shadow of a thought where a memory used to be. Sometimes, what I believed to be treasure is revealed as worthless. A curator's job is to constantly scrutinise their collection, whether it is fossils or memories. Still, throughout everything, my little ammonite sits on a shelf in the sunshine, waiting to be picked up.

I couldn't hear the past then, but I can now.

Deep Absence

By Alison Seller

Highly commended in poetry: 2017-18

No bones here.
No shell of skin, or feathers
brushed into the stone.
No marbled carapace, or
shale spiral.
Only outlines
traced in tropical sand
aeons past.
Now, like Pictish cup-marks, they
brim with soft Skye rain:
two footprints
one cradling the other.
An imprint of family.

Yet, here is deep absence.
A Jurassic mother and her hatchling
move on.
The record of life's urgency
pressed in stone.
And I recall
the melancholy of beaches,
our footprints

smoored by surf.
And, still, I see Hugh Miller,
who knew the worth and weight of stone.
I see him
lost and deep within his grief.
His fingers
tracing the letters he has hewn.
His sweet Elizabeth's name
preserved in tender stone.

No Ordinary Prize: On Winning the Hugh Miller Writing Competition 2017-18

By Alex Woodcock

The loose black shale pebble crumbled open after only a few tentative strikes with a harder, hand-sized rock, revealing two cream-coloured ammonite fossils. Somewhere behind me a dolphin eased itself to the surface of the still water. Eathie Beach, Saturday morning. It was not yet half past ten.

This is the thing, I thought, as I placed the fossils carefully in my bag: Hugh Miller was responsible for this, all of this. One long dead pioneering mutton-chopped polymath geologist stonemason had laid a thread from his life to mine across decades when neither of us were living. He couldn't have foreseen this moment, and indeed, only a few hours before neither could I. His words had found me though, and in them I'd found an ancient electricity, a charge, and had tried to hold an echo of their energy in words of my own. My words had, in their turn, connected with others. Some synergetic circuit had been completed and now there was movement. Specifically, to Cromarty, a weekend in which was my prize.

Just as there is often no logic to writing there must be similarly no logic to winning a writing prize. I guess that this applies as much to the complexities of judging entries as it does to the genesis of the entry. Sentences that had wound their way out of my pen one night while making notes for what I'd intended to be a piece of prose had refused, when I'd returned to them the following morning, to bend far from their staccato forms. I recognised the ghost of a poem spread across the litter of post-it notes on my desk and, fortunately, didn't press on with my original plans. Instead, I let it haunt.

The poem that emerged can be traced to a number of things. First was the plesiosaur. The competition logo featured the lovely outline of a somnambulant plesio with lazy fins and so I paid attention: these creatures and I go back a long way. I'd have been around five or six when I'd discovered dinosaurs and other extinct reptiles, and of them all the plesiosaur was, for me, among the best and most exciting. I loved the otherworldly shape of the creature, the perfect, graceful lines and curves. I had a blue plastic model of one bought from my beloved gift shop in London's Natural History Museum. I don't know what happened to that model, now long gone, but perhaps the memory of it was enough to get me to click on the link and investigate further.

My initial thought, however, was: this isn't for me. I knew nothing about the criteria for the competition – fossil discoveries in Scotland made during the last thirty years. But a few days later I found myself online, idly researching things. Hugh Miller, I discovered, had, among other things, been a stonemason. This made me sit up, as I am a stonemason too. I ordered one of his books, *My Schools and Schoolmasters*, and when it arrived began to read. In it he recounted how, while working on a job one day, he had been called by a local 'madwoman' a 'stonemason in disguise'; someone who was operating under the cover of being a stonemason but whose interests lay in many other places. She had seen beyond his trade and I warmed to that. In some respects, I think I might be a 'stonemason in disguise' too.

I started to search for fossil discoveries. Nothing really clicked, however, until I found out about *Pneumodesmus newmani*, an ancient millipede discovered in the rocks near Stonehaven in the early two-thousands. I knew Stonehaven: I had been to one of the best weddings of my life there, an event that has become semi-legendary in my mind both for the setting of the ceremony, Dunottar Castle, and the largesse of the hosts (as well as the crippling back injury from the violence of the ceilidh, the pain of which recurred for years). This seemed to present a chance to connect the personal with the long, geological durations of time that always seem to be so inaccessible and abstract. From that point on, I started to write.

I'm not in any sense a regular at the top of the pile, but from what I understand of them prizes usually come in the form of a defined thing: a sum of money perhaps or the presentation of an item. This one had included that as I'd been given a selection of books at the awards ceremony in Edinburgh. But, as I was soon to discover, it would go far beyond that too. It's not just that the Hugh Miller museum in Cromarty, closed for the season, was opened especially and a guided tour laid on; or that I was regularly fed incredible food and drinks and invited into people's – stranger's – homes and made to feel very welcome; or taken on a trip to find fossil-fish at the end of which I was given a specimen to take with me, just in case we hadn't found anything (we had); or taken around Cromarty and told its stories; or drunk ancient water from the artesian well. It's more that in among all this discovery and generosity and warmth and wonder was something that couldn't really be defined, much like Hugh Miller himself. The entire weekend seemed to exist according to its own laws, within its own time, as if connecting with the multiple interests and traces of the man had drawn us all into his mercurial orbit and we were now, ourselves, inhabiting a slightly altered state.

On the walk around Cromarty there had been talk of a mermaid. This was both a folkloric one as well as a 'real' one, carved in stone some centuries ago and set into a wall. I asked if we could go and see it. We walked through the nursery school garden, carefully stepping over toys and plants until we could get no closer to where it was set. A curtain of ivy hung over the stones obscuring everything. It couldn't be seen, but that didn't mean that it wasn't there. It hit me, then, what a prize this was. For a writer that spot where the stories live - that quicksilver between the past and the present, the formed and the formless - is imbued with a kind of magic. Here we were right in that spot, chasing the outline of a mermaid's tail, the story behind it still breathing among the stones.

And Hugh Miller was responsible for this, all of this.

Contributors

Ross Barnett earned his doctorate from the University of Oxford, studying the genetics of extinct cat species. For his work with educational charity The Brilliant Club, he received the 2018 Gertrude Elles Award for Public Engagement from the Palaeontological Association. His first book *The Missing Lynx* is due for publication by Bloomsbury in July 2019.

Simon Cuthbert is a geologist with thirty-five years' experience as a researcher, teacher and public science communicator, with interests including mountains, gold and other worlds. Simon's manifesto is that rocks speak to all of us; there are as many ways to hear their stories as there are those who will listen. He is a judge for the Hugh Miller Writing Competition.

Michael Davenport spent his childhood in Eyemouth, Berwickshire. Before retirement in 2001 he taught in the science departments of East Lothian's high schools. His interests include scuba diving and geology. His most recent poetry booklet *The Science of Lives* (2014) was published by Tyne and Esk Writers.

Bob Davidson MBE is a freelance well engineer working in the oil and gas industry for the past forty-four years. Married with two grown up children, he is the current chairman of the Friends of Hugh Miller and an Honorary research fellow at Aberdeen University. In 2018 he was awarded an MBE for his services to Scottish Palaeontology. He has written and co-authored over seventeen articles and papers on Scottish palaeontology, and is the holder of the inaugural Mary Anning Award from the Palaeontological Association for contributions to palaeontology.

Gillian Dawson grew up in Ayrshire and lives in Renfrewshire where she works in a library and writes poetry inspired by a love of the natural world. She has had haiku published in *Presence, Blithe Spirit and the Haiku Calendar 2018*.

Annabelle Fuller is currently a Classics and English student at Magdalen College, Oxford. She is a member of the Florio Society there and has had poems published in *New Poetry Magazine*, *CAKE*, and the *Society of Classical Poets Journal*. She won a BBC Proms Poetry Competition category in 2018.

Joyce Gilbert has worked in the field of environmental education for over thirty years and is interested in how people can reconnect with their cultural and natural heritage through outdoor experiences. Recently she has been exploring the use of story and journey to design unusual projects where learners of all ages can encounter a sense of place in new ways.

Jim Gilchrist is a freelance writer based in Portobello, Edinburgh (where Hugh Miller passed his last years).

He was for many years a staff features and arts writer with *The Scotsman*, to which he still contributes a music column, as well as writing for publications including the American-based *Scottish Life* magazine.

Martin Gostwick is a freelance journalist, born in London, England. He is a 'new' Scot, gratefully resident in this country since 1981. He founded the charity The Friends of Hugh Miller in 2006, and is the editor of its magazine, *Hugh's News*. He lives in Cromarty with his wife, Frieda, and both have been managers of the Hugh Miller Birthplace Cottage and Museum.

Thomas Halliday was born and raised in Edinburgh, via the Yorkshire Dales and Loch Rannoch. He is a palae-ontologist at the University of Birmingham, specialising in the evolution of mammals, particularly in the periods before and after the last mass extinction event. Thomas's upcoming book *Yesterday's Worlds: Travels in Earth's Extinct Ecosystems*, will be published by Penguin in 2021.

Paula Hunter grew up in Glasgow before defecting to Edinburgh. A lawyer, fundraiser, butcher and florist, her fiction has won the Brighton Story Prize, TSS flash monthly, placed second in Exeter Story Prize, and listed for Caledonia Novel Award and Stack Awards. She blogs at https://paula-hunter.com/ and tweets at @hillsnspills.

Robert Macfarlane is the author of several books on landscape, place, nature and people, including *Mountains of the Mind* (2003), *The Wild Places* (2007), *The Old Ways* (2012) and *Landmarks* (2015). He has just finished work on a book called *Underland*, about the worlds beneath our feet and sight, to be published by Penguin in 2019. He is a Fellow of Emmanuel College, Cambridge.

Jim Mackintosh's poem 'Old is Tomorrow' appears in his book *The Rubicon of Ash*. He is an active poet regularly performing across Festivals and Events and published his latest collection *Flipstones* in July 2018. Jim also champions the life and legacy of Perth born poet William Soutar, and is a member of the Hamish Matters Committee, which celebrates the life and legacy of Hamish Henderson.

Màiri Anna NicUalraig (Mary Ann Kennedy) is a Glasgow Gael living in Lochaber. She is a highly respected musician and broadcaster whose interest in words began with the great Gaelic song canon. Her own writing stems from a passion to connect with audiences through her mother-tongue and to assert Gaelic as a language of present and future.

Elsa Panciroli is a palaeontologist from the Scottish Highlands. She researches Jurassic mammals, and is part of ongoing palaeontological work in Scotland's Inner Hebrides. She is also a freelance writer and blogger, having contributed regularly to *The Guardian*, and other online and in-print publications. Elsa is a judge for the Hugh Miller Writing Competition.

Elizabeth Pickett worked for ten years as a field geologist in Scotland with the British Geological Survey. Now based in Northumberland, she is a freelance geologist, interpretive writer and illustrator. In 2015 she joined the Hugh Miller-inspired sea voyage around the Argyll islands.

Larissa (Lara) Reid is a freelance science writer and editor who has worked regularly with the Scottish Geodiversity Forum and The Friends of Hugh Miller for the past four years. She is the organiser and head judge of the Hugh Miller Writing Competition. She has recently published her first small volume of poetry, *In February*, and writes blog posts on themes related to geo-heritage, the natural world and mental health.

Mackenzie Erin Robbie moved to The Isle of Luing, Scotland with her family, including her four brothers, at the age of ten. She based her short story around this slate island. She wrote it when she was twelve years old – her mum and a local artist, Edna, were very supportive throughout the process.

Justin Sales is originally from Bristol, and now lives in Edinburgh where he teaches English for Speakers of Other Languages (ESOL), having previously worked in Thailand, Romania, China and Indonesia. He studied English in Aberdeen which he chose for its proximity to the hills. He recently built a bamboo bike which so far has not broken or been stolen.

Alison Seller's writing reflects her appreciation of the ordinary extraordinary, drawing inspiration from the natural world and philosophy. Alongside her poetry and short stories, she has written and performed dramatic monologues. She is privileged to live in the beautiful historic town of Cromarty.

Kenneth Steven is a full-time and widely published writer who grew up in Highland Perthshire. He is first and foremost a poet, but also a novelist and children's author. He now lives on the west coast of Scotland and is more and more involved with the island of Iona and a deeper understanding of the Celtic Christian story. www.kennethsteven.co.uk

Kenny Taylor writes and presents mainly non-fiction based on wildlife, science, culture and history in a variety of media. This includes magazines such as *BBC Wildlife* and *National Geographic* and scripts, interviews and performances for television, radio and theatre. He lives on the Black Isle and edits the literary magazine *Northwords Now*. Kenny is a judge for the Hugh Miller Writing Competition.

Michael Taylor is a Visiting Research Fellow at the School of Museum Studies, University of Leicester, and Research Associate at the Department of Natural Sciences, National Museums Scotland, Edinburgh. He is author of the standard modern biography *Hugh Miller: stonemason, geologist, writer*, and has contributed to various papers on Miller's life, work and fossil collections. Contact: mat22@le.ac.uk

Antonia Thomas is a Lecturer in Archaeology at Orkney College, part of the University of Highlands and Islands. Her research includes graffiti, prehistoric art, stone-carving, and the links between archaeology and contemporary art. She is also a Trustee of the Orkney Natural History Society Museum (Stromness Museum), where the celebrated Asterolepis of Stromness (*Homosteus milleri*) fossil is on permanent display.

Jane Verburg worked as a teacher for many years. These days she is found working in her silver jewellery studio in Miller's hometown of Cromarty. She has a great interest in the history of the town. Her writing has been acknowledged in many writing competitions, including the Neil Gunn and the Sir Thomas Urquhart.

Fiona Ritchie Walker's poetry has been widely published in magazines and anthologies. Her latest collection, *The Second Week of the Soap*, is published by Red Squirrel Press. A newspaper article and the challenge of this competition inspired her to write her first poem about geology.

Alex Woodcock is a writer and stonemason from the south coast of England. His books include *Gargoyles and Grotesques* and *Of Sirens and Centaurs*. His latest book, *King of Dust*, will be published by Little Toller this year.

References

Publications by Hugh Miller:

The Sketch-book of Popular Geology. (Edinburgh: Constable, 1859)

My Schools and Schoolmasters: or The Story of my Education. (Edinburgh: B&W Publishing, 1993). First published 1854

The Old Red Sandstone or New Walks in an Old Field. (London and Toronto: Everyman's Library and J.M. Dent & Sons Ltd, 1922). First published 1841

The Cruise of the Betsey, or A Summer Ramble Among the Fossiliferous Deposits of the Hebrides, and Rambles of a Geologist, or Ten Thousand Miles over the Fossiliferous Deposits of Scotland. (Edinburgh: NMS Publishing, 2003). Facsimile of text first published 1858

The Testimony of the Rocks or, Geology in Its Bearings on the Two Theologies, Natural and Revealed. (Huntingdon: St. Matthew Publishing, 2001). First published 1857

Essays, Historical and Biographical, Political and Social, Literary and Scientific. (Edinburgh: Black, 1862)

Publications referenced by Michael Taylor in *Hugh Miller's Palace of Printing*:

Forbes Gray, W., 'Old Edinburgh. Last of Horse Wynd', *The Scotsman*, 23 November, 1928, p. 7

Guthrie, D.K. and Guthrie, C.J., *Autobiography of Thomas Guthrie, D.D. and memoir by his sons*, 2 volumes. (New York: Carter 1874)

McKean, C., *The Making of the Museum of Scotland*. (Edinburgh: NMS Publishing, 2000)

McKean, C., 'A tale of two cities –a Dickens of a tale! Hugh Miller's Edinburgh', in Borley, L. (editor.) *Hugh Miller in context: geologist and naturalist: writer and folklorist*. (Cromarty: Cromarty Arts Trust, 2002), 85-91

Rainy, R. and Mackenzie, J., *Life of William Cunningham, D.D. Principal and Professor of Church History, New College, Edinburgh*. (London: Nelson, 1871)

Publications referenced by Bob Davidson in *Rambles of a Geologist*:

Page, D., *Handbook of Geological Terms. Geology and Physical Geography*. (Edinburgh and London: William Blackwood and Sons, 1865)

Publications referenced by Kenny Taylor in *Echoes from Orcadie*:

De Vleeschouwer, D., Leather, D. and Claeys, P., 'Ripple marks indicate Mid-Devonian paleo-wind directions in the Orcadian Basin (Orkney Isles, Scotland)', *Paleogeography, Palaeoclimatology, Palaeoecology*, 426, (2015), 68-74

Donovan, R.N., 'Lacustrine cycles, fish ecology and stratigraphic zonation in the Middle Devonian of Caithness', *Scottish Journal of Geology*, 16:1, (1980), 35-50

Stephenson, M.H., Leng, M.J., Michie, U. and Vane, C.H., 'Palaeolimnology of Palaeozoic lakes, focussing on a single lake cycle in the Middle Devonian of the Orcadian Basin, Scotland', *Earth Science Reviews*, 75, (2006), 177-197

Scottish Fossil Code

Scotland has a remarkable diversity of fossils stretching back over 1200 million years. Fossil collecting as a hobby can contribute to the science of palaeontology.

The Scottish Fossil Code encourages responsible fossil collecting. It also aims to enhance public interest in Scotland's fossil heritage and promote this resource for scientific, educational, and recreational purposes.

If collecting fossils in Scotland, please do so responsibly and follow the best practice advice outlined in the Scottish Fossil Code.

Find out more from
www.nature.scot.

Scottish Natural Heritage
Dualchas Nàdair na h-Alba
nature.scot